MW00932720

LIVING IN HOPE

Living in hope

Mary Weeks Millard

DERNIER PUBLISHING
Tonbridge

First published 2011

Published by Dernier Publishing
P.O. Box 403, Tonbridge, TN9 9BJ, England
www.dernierpublishing.com

ISBN: 978 0 9569043 0 0

Book design and production for the publisher by
Bookprint Creative Services, <www.bookprint.co.uk>
Printed in Great Britain.

To Sophie and Matthew,
two special godchildren who have learnt to care
both about the people and the animals
of Rwanda

Acknowledgements

My grateful thanks to my ever-patient husband, Malcolm, who encourages me to continue writing and also to Janet Evans of Dernier Publishing for all her help and support in the production of this book.

ONE

Starting School

Shema woke as soon as it was light. He was so excited! Today was the first day of the new school term and he was going to school for the first time in his life, even though he was almost ten years old!

Shema was an orphan. His parents had both been killed in the terrible war which had swept through his country of Rwanda when he was very young. Since then he had lived with his older sister, Ishimwe, who was now twelve, and his younger brother, Maji, who was six. For a long time after the war the children had struggled to survive, living in an old, leaky, mud-brick house and had only just managed to get enough food to eat. Ishimwe had looked after her brothers as well as she could, even though she was only a girl. Instead of going to school, Shema had looked after goats for a neighbour, to earn a little money. But a year ago their lives had changed for the better; they were given a brand new home in a village called "Hope", which had been built especially for children like themselves, who had no grown-ups to care for them. They were so excited to move into their lovely new home!

There were thirty houses in the village, built in neat rows, each with its own little garden for growing vegetables, and outhouses for cooking and washing. Most of the children who lived there had planted evergreen shrubs around their homes, making the compound look neat and tidy. Some had managed to buy a chicken or a goat, and the shrub hedge helped keep them from wandering away!

There was one larger house in the village, which belonged to the social worker, Delphine, whom the children called "Auntie". The children lived independent lives, but Delphine was always there to help them if they needed anything. She sorted out all the charity money that was sent to pay for their schooling, too. Delphine was a plump, jolly young lady and the children loved her very much.

Ishimwe had learnt to use a sewing machine last year and was now a very good dressmaker. She had sewn Shema a school shirt and shorts in the regulation khaki material which all Rwandan primary school boys wear. Shema could hardly wait to wear it on that first day of term! It was on the stool next to his bed, ready for him to put on. First, however, he had to go and fetch the water the family would need for the day. Even this was not such hard work as it used to be in the old house, because the well was so much nearer and it wasn't such a hilly walk! Cheerfully Shema pulled on his old clothes, picked up the yellow plastic can and ran to the village well. Many other children from the Village of Hope were there too.

"New school year starts today!" he was reminded by one of the big boys of the village. "You're going today, aren't you?"

"Yes, I can't wait!" replied Shema. "I've been wanting to go to school for years. I want to study and one day become an airline pilot."

The other boy laughed. "You will have to be very clever to get a job like that!"

Back at the house Ishimwe was busy making breakfast. Maji was tearing round the house cheerfully as usual. Although he was six now, there was not enough money for him to start school yet; he would have to wait until Delphine could find him a sponsor or Ishimwe could make enough money by selling the clothes she made.

Shema gobbled down his porridge made from ground millet, quickly washed his face and hands and changed into his smart new uniform. Waving goodbye to his brother and sister, he began the long walk down the path which led to his old village where Sam, his best friend, lived. Shema didn't mind walking a long way! He was so grateful to one of the teachers at the school there, who had become his friend and kindly taught him to read and write.

Sam lived with his mother and her parents. Sam's father had been killed in the war. His older sister, Grace, went to boarding school in the capital city, Kigali, because there was no senior school in the area.

As is the custom, their mother was known by the name of her first child, and so was called "Mama Grace".

Sam was waiting for Shema to arrive and so was Mama Grace! She knew what a special day this was for Shema and greeted him with a big hug. "How smart you look in your uniform! Wait here a moment, I have a little gift for you." Mama Grace popped inside her house and came out with an exercise book and a pencil. "Here you are, you will need these!"

Shema squealed with delight. "Thank you so much!" He put the pencil carefully in his pocket and balanced the exercise book on his head, just like Sam.

"Do you know which class you will be in?" asked Sam, as the friends began to walk up the hill to the school.

"Yes," answered Shema, "I am to try Class Two. I am going to work very hard and catch you up though!"

Sam had been at school for several years now and was about to enter Class Four. In Rwanda you don't go up into the next class until you have passed an exam to show you have reached the correct standard, so Shema couldn't start in Class Four with Sam, even though they were the same age.

As they got nearer the school, they were joined by many other children; the boys in their khaki uniforms and the girls in bright blue cotton dresses. Although Shema felt a bit nervous, he thought his heart might burst with happiness at being part of the crowd of laughing, chattering schoolchildren.

The school was a long building, divided into seven classrooms. It was built of mud bricks, but had been nicely whitewashed and gleamed in the morning sun. Each class teacher stood outside their door and welcomed the pupils as they arrived, checking their names against the register. Inside, the classrooms were quite bare; no pictures on the walls, just a blackboard that stretched across the whole of the front wall. The desks were built for two children, but because of numbers, three children had to squeeze in together. They didn't mind, they were just pleased to be at school!

Shema went to Class Two. The teacher was called Mrs Mugisha, and she greeted him kindly. He was asked to sit in the front row, between a boy called Bosco and a girl called Agnes. They both looked at the newcomer and smiled. As Shema looked around the class, he recognised a few faces from the time when he was a goatherd and brought his flock to graze near the school. Everyone seemed very friendly and Shema felt his nervousness disappear. Mrs Mugisha greeted the class in their native language, Kinyarwanda. They all stood up politely and greeted her back.

"Sit down please," she said to them with a smile. "Our first lesson today is to learn how to greet in both French and English!" Soon the children were repeating after her, "Bonjour, Madame Mugisha," and "Good morning, Mrs Mugisha." It sounded very strange to Shema, who had not heard either language before. Soon, however, they moved on to maths and reading, which he found much easier, thanks to his teacher friend who had helped him so much. In what seemed like no time at all it was break, and Shema rushed outside to play football with Sam. School was great!

After the break, the headmaster came to the classroom and asked Shema to come with him. Shema began to tremble. Perhaps he wasn't going to be allowed to stay at school! Perhaps, after all, he might have to start in the first class with all the other new children? The headmaster smiled at Shema kindly. "Don't worry," he told him, "we have government rules to keep. Before you enter Class Two you must pass the leaving examination for Class One. I thought you could come and do it now."

The headmaster led Shema into his office. "Do you have a pencil?" asked the headmaster.

"Yes sir," answered Shema, taking the beautiful new pencil that Mama Grace had given him out of his pocket. By now Shema had begun to shake again. He had never taken an exam before and didn't know what to do, but the headmaster sat him down at a little table by the window and smiled kindly. He gave Shema a sheet of paper with lots of writing on it.

"All you do is answer the questions. The way to do it is to read the question twice. When you are sure you understand, tick the right box or write down the answer. When you have finished, there is another piece of paper with maths. Don't worry, I think you will find it all very easy! I know the Class Four teacher who has been helping you is sure you will do well!"

Shema looked at the paper and in his head he prayed a prayer. "Dear Mister God, please help me do this. Amen." Once he had started, Shema found he was enjoying doing the exam! He remembered to do what he was told and read through the question twice, thinking carefully before putting the answer down. The headmaster was right, it was quite easy! Soon Shema was doing the maths paper and he liked that. The headmaster was pleased because he finished quickly.

"Well done!" he said to Shema. "Go back to your class now, but come to me just before you go home and I will tell you if you have passed."

The rest of the day passed quickly. Shema made friends with Bosco and Agnes and played with them and Sam in the lunch break. All too soon it was time to go home. Sam was waiting for him as he came out of the class.

"First I have to go to the headmaster," Shema explained. "I have to get the result of my exam. I do hope I have passed and can stay in Class Two!"

The headmaster was waiting for him, along with the teacher of Class Four who had taught him to read and write. "We are very proud of you, Shema!" the teacher said. "You have done very well in the exam. In fact, you were better than any of last year's Class One pupils!"

The headmaster nodded. "I am sending the paper to the government office and you are officially in Class Two! Keep on working like this and you will be a credit to our school," he added.

"I will sir, I really will!" answered Shema. He ran happily out of the office to share the results with Sam.

What a great day his first day at school had been!

TWO

Ishimwe's Day

While Shema was enjoying his first day at school, Ishimwe had been busy. It was market day in the nearest town, so she was off to sell the clothes she had made. As soon as she had tidied the house, she took Maji around to her next door neighbour, Frida, who was thirteen years old and, like Ishimwe, took care of her younger sister and brother. Frida's sister Janette was eleven and went to school, but like Maji, her little six-year-old brother Michal stayed at home. Maji and Michal were best friends and Frida was happy to look after Maji when Ishimwe went to market. In return, Ishimwe would do any shopping Frida needed; or if she had any fruit or vegetables to sell, she sold them for her. Maji was much happier playing with Michal than sitting in the sun at the market all day!

Ishimwe tied her clothes into a neat bundle, which she wrapped in a cloth and balanced on her head. She took a large, brightly coloured umbrella with her, not because it might rain, but because it was very hot sitting in the sun selling her clothes, and she could use it as a sunshade! She sang as she walked along the dusty road. Life was so much better since she and her brothers had been given a house in the Village of Hope!

Soon she arrived at the market town and found a place where she could lay out her clothes on the cloth. She did it as neatly as she could, then quietly said a prayer asking her Father, God, to help her sell the things she had made.

Very soon a large lady with a baby on her back came along and started examining the school dresses Ishimwe had made. "These are beautifully finished," she said. "You are a good dressmaker!"

"Thank you," answered Ishimwe shyly.

The large lady was struggling to bend down to see the clothes with her baby on her back. "May I lay baby down on your cloth while I look to find the right size for my daughter?" she asked.

"Of course Mama. Please let me put up my umbrella to shade her while you look," Ishimwe answered politely. The large lady was pleased, and once her baby was settled, she sorted through the school dresses and chose two! Then she looked at some baby dresses and chose one of those as well. She turned to Ishimwe and asked her if she could make her a blouse and skirt for a special occasion.

"Gladly," replied Ishimwe. "Why don't you go to the material stall and choose some fabric, then come back and I will measure you. I can have the skirt and blouse ready for you next week, if you like?"

The lady smiled and nodded. She paid for the three dresses she had already chosen, then Ishimwe helped her put her baby on her back and she went off to choose material. In no time at all she was back with some bright yellow and red fabric. She was the largest woman that Ishimwe had ever measured and Ishimwe was glad to see she had bought a lot of cloth! "I will come back to collect my clothes next week. Thank you my dear," the lady said to Ishimwe, and went away smiling.

By this time it was hot and Ishimwe was thirsty. She had some water with her and was glad to have a drink and sit under the shade of her umbrella. Most of the women around her knew and admired Ishimwe, impressed by her hard work to support her family. Next to her was a young mother who was selling tomatoes. Frida needed some; so Ishimwe bought some for her and some for herself. Tomatoes would be lovely with their beans and rice for supper!

After a little while another two ladies came to look at her sewing. One wanted a school uniform for her boy and the other wanted a skirt. The lady wanting the skirt couldn't make up her mind which one she liked the most, so bought two! It was proving a very good day for sales! When it was time to pack up, Ishimwe had sold almost every garment she had made! She was very excited. She also had the order for the large lady's blouse and skirt. She wrapped the red and yellow material very carefully in her cloth, picked up the tomatoes and her umbrella and started home. It had been one of the best days she had ever had at the market! She thanked God as she walked along the road. She was trying to save a little money for a secret special treat for her family, and just the thought of it made her smile. Maybe she would share her secret with Mama Grace! There was just time to go and visit her before she went home.

Mama Grace was sitting with the Old People, as her parents were called. They had just made some tea and were very pleased to see Shema's sister.

"I've had such a good day at the market!" Ishimwe told them excitedly. "I sold almost all my clothes and have a good order for next week." She undid the parcel and showed them the red and yellow fabric. She also showed Mama Grace the measurements which she had written on a piece of paper and pinned to the cloth. "You see, she was a very large lady!"

Ishimwe left the fabric near Mama Grace's sewing machine, which she borrowed to do her work.

"I will make the pattern for you tonight, if you like, so that you can begin in the morning," offered the Old Lady, who loved to help her young friend.

"Oh thank you so much," said Ishimwe, "What would I do without you all! And listen, I want to tell you about an idea I have had. If I can save enough money, I'd like to buy Shema and Maji a chicken each as a present for Christmas!"

Everyone clapped in approval. "That's a lovely idea, they will love that," said Mama Grace. The Old People nodded too.

Ishimwe smiled. "And we will be able to have fresh eggs, too! It's a secret, so please don't tell anyone."

When she arrived home Ishimwe went to collect Maji from next door. She found Frida already cooking supper for her family. Frida was really pleased with the tomatoes from the market and made a cup of tea so that they could sit and chat.

Frida was cross that her life had turned out the way it had, and talking to Ishimwe helped her forget her troubles for a while. She was resentful that she couldn't go to school or learn to be a hairdresser because she had to look after Janette and Michal. Since Ishimwe and the boys had come to live next door, she had enjoyed having a friend so much. Sometimes, when all the work was done, they would play together with a home-made skipping rope, which was a vine cut from a tree. It was fun to be children together rather than always having to work like grown-ups. Ishimwe seemed always to be happy and laughing, and usually managed to cheer Frida up.

On Sundays, when Ishimwe, Shema and Maji went to church in the next village, they always invited Frida, Janette and Michal to go with them. Frida wasn't interested, but was glad her brother and sister went, as it gave her time to laze around on her own.

THREE

Frida's Problems

On the second day of the school term Frida woke up with a terrible headache. She had been troubled by awful dreams in the night. She often had them and they were always the same. Michal was on her back and Janette was holding on to her skirt and they were running, running, running. She could hear the screams as soldiers were attacking her village, and she was running away into the banana plantation to hide.

The screams would fade and Frida would wake up in a sweat and with a headache, like this morning. It took her back to the war when her parents, and, as far as she knew, all her relatives, were killed – simply because they belonged to the wrong racial group. "Why do people hate each other so much?" she wondered wearily. That war had changed her life for ever. She had never been able to go back to school and her life now was to be mother to Michal and Janette.

She had been glad when workers from the charity who built the Village of Hope had found them living in an old mud hut in the middle of a swamp. Michal had been very thin and kept getting malaria because of the mosquitoes in the swamp. Frida had tried to grow a few vegetables and millet to feed them all, but it had been hard work. Life improved a lot when they were given a home in the Village of Hope, and it had got even better when Ishimwe and her brothers had moved in next door. It was great to have a friend her own age!

Even so, Frida felt angry inside. She didn't think it was fair that she had to be the mother. Janette went to school and could already read and write better than she did. Next term Michal would go as well, because they had heard that a family in Europe was willing to sponsor him. But what about her? Would she spend the rest of her life as a peasant girl, growing vegetables? She was already thirteen and becoming a pretty young lady, but how could she get a good job with no education and two children to support?

Frida couldn't understand why Ishimwe was always so cheerful. She knew her friend had a secret longing to be a nurse, but she couldn't possibly do that, because she couldn't go to school either. She didn't complain about looking after Shema and Maji or doing all the cleaning and cooking. She worked so hard at her sewing, too. Frida was a bit jealous of that, even though Ishimwe was very generous to her and made clothes for her and her family.

Frida knew that going to church had made a difference to Ishimwe, because Ishimwe had told her, but she herself was angry with God and felt that he couldn't love her, otherwise he would have saved her parents and given her a good life.

Frida sighed. It was getting light and she must get up and light the fire in the little hut outside which served as her kitchen. A bowl of millet porridge and a cup of tea would cheer her up! She called Janette and sent her to the well for water and then woke up Michal. He could see his sister was in a bad mood and quickly got washed and dressed. He was planning to go with Maji to the pond at the end of the village and look for frogs. They loved watching the frogs jump around!

While Frida was cooking the millet she had a strange feeling that someone was watching her. She looked over the small hedge which she had planted around the house and saw a tall man walking along the path. Somehow it made her feel a bit uneasy, but many people walked through the village, so she told herself not to be silly, and called the children for their breakfast.

Soon Janette had left for school and Michal went out to play. Frida went to the bedroom which she shared with Janette and tidied the mattress and blankets. Then she got the brush made from twigs tied together and swept the floors. The work made her feel a bit better. Next, Frida got a bowl of water and began to wash the clothes. She had one tiny piece of soap which she rubbed carefully on the cloth. "I must make this last another week," she said to herself with a sigh as she rinsed the clothes carefully, and then hung them on a line which had been fixed between her house and Ishimwe's. She used to put the washing on the hedge to dry, but the social worker, Delphine, had taught them that it was much better to hang the clothes up and had helped the children put up string washing lines. Frida looked at the clothes and thought what a good idea it was to hang them up. She felt pleased at how clean they looked in spite of so little soap.

Now it was time to start soaking the dried beans for the evening meal. "Beans and rice again," she thought with a sigh as she looked into her tiny store. She washed the rice several times to get rid of grit and dirt. With a tomato and half an onion she had saved from the day before, Frida decided to make a little sauce to go with the rice and beans. It wasn't much, but it would have to do! At least the millet was growing well and her vegetable garden was in order. If the rains came on time then they should have a good harvest in a few months.

Thinking about food had made her headache worse, so Frida put some water to boil in a pan and went next door to see if Ishimwe wanted some tea.

"Ishy, I'm boiling some water to brew a little tea," she called over the hedge to her friend.

"Great," came the reply. "I'll bring a spoonful of sugar to add to the tea leaves for a treat!"

The girls had no milk, just a very few tea leaves which they put into the pan of water and added the sugar. It might not sound very nice, but they loved it! Afterwards they played for a while with their skipping rope before going to collect firewood to use for cooking that evening. It was always hard work finding firewood, but much more fun doing it together. On the way back they stopped at the pond where Maji and Michal were playing, to make sure the two boys were being good.

Once back at home, Frida again had that strange feeling that she was being watched, but no one was in sight. Maybe she was just tired after her bad night, she decided. If only her life could be different! She began to daydream about being a hairdresser in a big city with many important and famous customers coming to her shop! If she had the chance she would be the best hairdresser in the country and maybe even the President's wife would visit her salon! She could see the shop with a sign over it saying "Frida's High Class Salon" . . .

If only!

FOUR

Sam in Trouble

Shema loved school! Each day seemed like a new adventure for him. There was so much to learn. Sometimes at break he would hear an aeroplane, watch it fly over and dream his dream of being an airline pilot. Suddenly it all seemed possible! Because the teacher who had befriended him when he was just a little goatherd had taught him so well, he was almost always able to answer the teacher's questions. He loved sport, too. The school had an area marked out as a football pitch. There was no grass, just dry earth, but the boys didn't mind; they could still kick their balls around. Most of them had home-made balls. They made them by winding twine from vines around bundles of rags, paper or anything else they could find. They didn't bounce, and didn't last very long, but were better than nothing.

There was one boy in Sam's class who did have a proper ball. It wasn't a football, but it was quite a big red rubber ball and, naturally enough, he was very proud of it. Gregoire was quite big for his age and a bit of a bully. He was also selfish. Sam asked one day if he could have a turn, but Gregoire refused to let him play with it. He always boasted how good he was at football, but in fact, he wasn't that good, and had not been picked for the school team.

It was a new idea to have a school football team, and the headmaster was very keen to enter the school into the newly-formed schools' league. If they were good enough and won the district games, they would be able to play the finals in the Amohoro stadium in Kigali, the capital city! The headmaster had a dream, too, that everyone would hear about his little village school because of its excellence!

Sam was the best footballer in the school and had not only been picked for the team, but had been made captain! Shema was very happy for his friend and proud of him. When there was time after lessons, he loved to play with Sam and help him improve his skills. Shema wasn't in the school team, but he didn't mind because he was only in Year Two; maybe next year he would be good enough. He was just happy to be at school!

One day Shema was surprised that Sam didn't join him at break time. He wondered what had happened because the two boys always played football together. "Maybe he is helping his teacher with something," he thought to himself. However, when it was lunch time, Sam still didn't appear, so Shema ate his banana and drank his little bottle of water on his own. Then Gregoire swaggered over to him, towering above him.

"Missing your friend, are you?" he said to Shema.

"Well, I was wondering where he is," Shema admitted. "We usually eat together."

"He's where he ought to be, kept in and in disgrace!" Gregoire said. "He's nothing but a common thief!"

"Thief?" Shema almost shouted in his surprise and anger. "Sam is no thief! I know him too well. He would never steal anything!"

"Wouldn't he?" sneered Gregoire. "Then how was my red ball found in his desk? Ask him that and see what he has to say! He said before he wanted to play with it, now he's stolen it." Gregoire walked away with a strange smile of satisfaction on his face. It left Shema feeling very troubled. That afternoon, for the first time since he had started school, he found it hard to concentrate on his lessons. There must have been some mistake! Sam would never steal anyone's ball!

After classes were finished, Shema waited outside Sam's classroom door for his friend. He was the last child to come out and his head was down and he looked very upset. Shema put his arm around his friend.

"Gregoire told me you were in trouble," he said. "He told me you had stolen his red ball. I told him there must be a mistake because you would never steal anything."

"It has been a terrible day," Sam replied, "almost the worst day I can remember. Thank you for believing in me. Everyone else thinks I am a thief!"

"What happened?" asked Shema.

"This morning after registration, Gregoire told our teacher that his red ball had been stolen. At first teacher thought he must just have lost it, but Gregoire insisted that a thief had taken it. He said he was sure that someone had it hidden in their desk. We all had to open the desks, and there it was in mine! Everyone turned and looked at me. It was horrible. I am the only one at my desk at the moment because Suzanne is sick and Petero can't pay his fees and so can't come. I was horrified! I could not believe my eyes! How had that ball got into my desk? The teacher told me to stay in through the breaks and he would see the headmaster about my punishment. He questioned me carefully, but although I told him I knew nothing about the ball, he sadly shook his head and said, 'The evidence is there Sam. I know you are a good boy, but sometimes, even good children are tempted.' I nearly cried when he said that because I thought that even he had doubts about me."

Shema's eyes grew wide in shock. "At lunch time," Sam continued, "the very worst thing happened. The headmaster has banned me from playing in the school football team because of it, even though I am one of the best players and the captain."

Sam was trying not to cry, but one or two tears did slide down his cheeks. He rubbed his eyes with the back of his hand. "Someone must have put that ball in my desk, but how can I prove it? Everyone now thinks I am a thief!"

"I don't," said Shema stoutly. "I know you would never steal. I will tell everyone so, too. I will try to prove you are innocent!"

"Thank you, Shema. I am so glad you are my friend. How am I going to tell my mother what has happened? Whatever will she think of me?"

"Just tell her what happened, just like you told me. She will believe you. She knows you wouldn't steal!"

The two boys walked slowly down the path and when they reached Sam's house Shema gave his friend's hand a big squeeze. "Father God knows who took the ball, so let's ask him to sort it out." They said a little prayer together and then Sam went to talk to his mother while Shema went on to his own village. He thought to himself as he went home that maybe he would tell his policeman friend when he went to help his wife; which he did each day as an after school job. Perhaps the policeman would know what to do.

For several days it was hard for Sam at school, because Gregoire pointed the finger at him and shouted, "Watch out, here comes the thief," whenever he walked past. He also found it so hard to watch the school team practising football, and see that Gregoire had taken his place. He wanted to shout back that it wasn't fair because he had not stolen the ball!

Shema was right about one thing. Mama Grace and her parents listened to Sam's story and believed him completely. That comforted him. Sam's grandmother, the Old Lady, reminded him that even Jesus was falsely accused. They prayed for Sam to have courage and not react badly.

Meanwhile, Shema was as good as his word. He talked to the policeman about Sam's problem, who listened very carefully. He told Shema to be patient, because the truth would eventually come out. He advised him to listen well when the children were outside at break time or walking to school, because someone would eventually boast about hiding the ball in Sam's desk. Also, it would be a good idea to think about who might have a reason for falsely accusing Sam.

So Shema began to listen to the children in Sam's class when they were chatting together, as well as making sure he played with Sam so that he didn't lose his football skills!

FIVE

Frida's Decision

A couple of weeks had passed since Frida had her terrible nightmare and bad day. From time to time Frida had noticed the stranger walking around the village, but decided it was none of her business. Maybe he was a friend of the social worker, Delphine; perhaps he wanted to marry her! She giggled at this thought!

On Sunday morning Janette and Michal went to church with Ishimwe, Shema and Maji. They had all been invited to Mama Grace's for a meal afterwards, but Frida had decided not to go. Having a nice meal was tempting, but so was a whole day by herself to laze around and daydream. If the children had a big meal at lunch time, she thought to herself, she wouldn't even have to bother much with supper!

After taking a long time to wash her hair and try a new hair style, Frida sat down in her living room with a cup of tea. She was startled by a knock at the door and a man's voice calling, "Can I come in?" Without thinking Frida automatically gave the usual reply.

"You are welcome," she said. In walked a tall, thin

man. Frida instantly recognised him as the man she had seen walking around the village recently.

"You will wonder who I am, Frida," he said.

"How do you know my name?" she asked in surprise.

"I am Justin, a cousin on your father's side," the man explained. "I found out that you are still alive and over the past couple of weeks I have watched and seen you are a good girl. You have grown up very well and are a credit to our family. I live in the capital city, Kigali, with my wife Penina and our baby boy Manweli. My dear wife is sick and weak. I badly need someone to help her and to care for our baby son. I have come to ask you to help us in our time of need. I will take care of you and you will have opportunities to live in the city and meet people. What do you think?"

Frida was flustered. "But I look after my brother and sister," she said. "I am not sure I can leave them."

"Your sister Janette is now a big girl. Surely she can take care of Michal and let you have a chance in life. You are a very pretty girl; you deserve a chance!"

At this Frida found herself blushing, although she knew it was true. Her father had always called her "my beauty", even when she was small. "When would you need me to come?" she asked.

"You have two hours to make up your mind," replied Justin. "I shall return with my car in two hours, and if you are coming, then have your things packed." With this, he got up and left.

After he had gone Frida sat down and put her head into her hands. She was in a turmoil. Was this the great opportunity that she had always dreamed about? If she said "no" to her cousin, would she ever get another chance? If she said "yes", would Janette and Michal cope at home?

Suddenly she wished that Ishimwe was at home so she could ask her opinion. It was Delphine's day off, too – so she couldn't talk to her, either. Two hours to decide! Frida realised that time was passing quickly by; she must make up her mind! She looked around the little house and it made her think how poor they were. Maybe she could earn a living in Kigali and send money home to the others. Perhaps she could learn to be a hairdresser and meet famous people, just like in her dream! She deserved a chance in life, she assured herself. She had made up her mind. She would go!

She gathered together the few clothes she had and tied them into a bundle. As she did so she noticed her twine skipping rope and gave a little sigh, knowing that she would have to leave what remained of her childhood behind. She would have to be grown up and responsible in the big city! She was really sorry not to be able to say goodbye to Janette, Michal and her friends and explain what was happening, but decided to write a note. The only paper they had was Janette's exercise book from school, but she wouldn't be needing that any more, she would have to be mother to Michal now! Frida tore out a sheet and found a pencil. She had only learnt a little in school herself, a very long time ago, and so struggled to write a letter.

"I am leavin for the city, Kigali. I will live with cusin Justin to hulp wife and bebe. Be good. Luv Frida."

It took her a long time to do this and she had just put the letter on her bed when she heard a car. Leaving the house unlocked she grabbed her bundle and got in beside her cousin.

"Good," he said with a smile. "You have decided well."

Frida smiled, but deep down she wasn't so sure. Part of her was excited at the prospect of a new life, but part of her was afraid. She had always lived in the country and only knew country ways and all of a sudden felt really bad at leaving Janette to care for Michal. And she did wish she could have talked to them and hugged them goodbye instead of just leaving a note!

It was too late to change her mind now though. Soon they were speeding out of the village and down to the main road, red dust flying all around them. Frida had hardly ever been in a car, and she couldn't help feeling a bit excited as the countryside sped past. Justin didn't talk very much to her. He stopped after about an hour and bought her a cold drink. That was a very special treat! "Will my life be full of treats from now on?" Frida wondered.

That thought pleased her very much. They set off again and this time the road was black tarmac, not red, dusty earth. After an hour or so they arrived in the outskirts of the city. Frida could see many large buildings, and they were mostly built of bricks or cement. She looked at everything with awe and amazement. The world suddenly seemed full of people in cars and on bicycles, lights flashing at junctions, policemen with whistles, people walking on pavements, and so much noise! At one point she found herself putting her hands over her ears to try to stop the noise getting to her head; but it didn't help much! Eventually they turned off the main road and drove up a mud track. Here the houses were little more than shacks, not half as nice as the houses in the Village of Hope. Justin put his foot on the brake and stopped outside a very shabby-looking house.

"Here we are!" he said. "Get your things and come and meet your mistress, Cousin Penina. You will be her maid."

Frida's heart sank. This wasn't what she had expected at all! Suddenly she knew she had made a big mistake.

SIX

Everything Changes

Janette, Michal, Ishimwe, Shema and Maji were singing as they walked from Mama Grace's house to their own village. They had enjoyed themselves at church and then had a wonderful meal with Sam and his family. Mama Grace had cooked chicken with their vegetables and rice; what a treat for them all to have meat!

"I hope Frida has had a nice, quiet day," Ishimwe said to Janette as they neared the village.

"I hope so, too," answered Janette. "She's been really grumpy lately. Maybe she needed a rest."

They reached the village and the children said goodbye to each other and went to their houses. Ishimwe had only just unlocked her door when Janette and Michal came running round to her house to say they could not find Frida; that all her things were gone and she had left a strange note.

Ishimwe was alarmed when she read the note. It seemed as if Frida had run away to Kigali. "Who is this cousin Justin?" she asked Janette.

"I don't know. I didn't think we had any relatives alive."

"Well," said Ishimwe, thinking aloud, "The day is almost over. Auntie is off duty today, so we can't ask her. Maybe, just for tonight, why don't you bring your mattresses and blankets over here for a sleepover? Then tomorrow we can talk to Delphine and get her advice."

Ishimwe didn't sleep well that night. She was troubled about her friend. She knew Frida was often unhappy and suffered from terrible nightmares about the war. But if she wasn't coming back, how would Janette and Michal manage? Ishimwe decided to talk to God about it all. He had helped so much when her family had difficult problems. Now she asked him to help these children, too.

The next morning, when all the children were up and dressed, Ishimwe sent the boys to fetch water for both houses. Shema got ready for school as usual, but Janette realised she would have to stay at home and take Frida's place, looking after Michal and doing all the housework. She felt sad, because she loved school and her friends there, but what else could she do?

When the girls had tidied up both houses, Ishimwe went with Janette and the boys to see Delphine, taking with them the note Frida had left.

Delphine listened carefully to what Janette had to say and read the note. She shook her head gravely. "We have no record of any of your relatives still being alive," she said to Janette. "I wonder how this cousin Justin found Frida living here – your parents didn't live in this area. I shall have to make enquiries in Kigali, but you will have to be patient because it may take a while. We shall do all we can to contact Frida and make sure she is safe and well."

Then she looked at Janette, who was trying not to cry. "I'm afraid that you will have to be 'mother' now to Michal. Can you manage that? He will need you very much in these days while we try to find Frida. You will have to try to be brave and grown up. I know Ishimwe will help you when she can and we will too."

"I'll try," said Janette, putting an arm around Michal to reassure him.

The next few days were hard for them all. Ishimwe tried to help Janette to get organised. There were many daily chores to be done; cleaning, finding firewood, cooking, looking after the garden as well as getting water and washing clothes. The only money Janette and Michal had was from selling a little garden produce at the market. How would they manage?

Ishimwe tried to think of ways she could help her neighbours. One idea she had was that the two families could eat together in the evenings. That would only mean one fire to light, and they could share the cooking. After the meal, the younger children could do the dishes while she would have time to teach Janette to weave baskets from the strong grass which grew by the river. Only recently Mama Grace's mother, the Old Lady, had shown her how to make them. If

Janette did well, maybe she could sell the baskets in the market to make money. Janette was only eleven and would need lots of help though! And there was another problem – who would look after the youngest boys on market days? Ishimwe decided to talk to Mama Grace about it, because she was so wise and caring.

When Mama Grace heard about Frida leaving home, she found herself crying for these poor children who had to work so hard just to survive. Then she called the Old People and they all prayed together. It was Sam's grandfather who came up with the best idea.

"I'm finding it more difficult to manage my little garden now I'm getting older," he said, "Why don't Maji and Michal come and help me and I will teach them how to grow good crops. Why, I can even teach them how to look after our cow and the chickens! While the boys are here out of the way, Janette will have more time in the house or to make baskets and Ishimwe will be able to continue dressmaking and go to the market without worrying about Maji being safe!"

This idea worked well. After a while the two families began to settle down again, although they all missed Frida so much. Ishimwe still played skipping sometimes with Janette, but it wasn't the same. She so longed to hear news of her friend.

Delphine had been doing her best to find news, but no one in the charity or in the local villages seemed to know who Justin was, or where he lived. She promised not to give up looking but couldn't give the children much hope of finding their sister. As she said, the policy in the village had always been that the children were free to live their own lives. It was not an orphanage, but a place of shelter.

Shema had his own problems, too. He was determined to find out who had put Gregoire's ball in Sam's desk. He did as his policeman friend had advised, and listened to the children in Sam's class, in case anyone boasted about playing a trick on Sam. He hated to see his friend so downcast and banned from the football team. The only person who didn't like Sam and was jealous of his football skills was Gregoire himself. He was the one who had gained a place in the team when Sam was punished. Could Gregoire himself have put the ball into Sam's desk? The more Shema thought about it, the more possible it seemed. But he had no proof.

Sometimes when he was working at the policeman's house after school, he chatted about his suspicions. The policeman warned him to be careful. "Do not accuse this boy unless you are absolutely certain, because you might be wrong and that could cause even more trouble. Try to be patient and keep listening."

The school football team were having problems, too. They missed their star player! Gregoire was by no means as good as Sam and the tournament prospects didn't look good without him.

One day, Shema had a breakthrough! He had gone to the toilet block which was at the end of the football pitch. Round the corner he heard a boy talking.

"You are useless! We always lose our matches because you can't score goals!" the boy was saying crossly.

"How dare you blame me!" Shema heard Gregoire saying, "Watch out! Or I'll get you out of the team, just like I got rid of someone else! You don't mess with people like me!"

Shema gasped! So, it was as he had thought! He was just about to rush to tell Sam's teacher what he had heard, when he suddenly thought, "They may think I have made up the story because I am Sam's friend." So he decided to walk straight round the corner and see who it was that Gregoire was talking with, and to his surprise it was Bosco, who shared his desk.

"Hi Bosco, you all right?" he asked cheerily.

"Yes, fine!" Bosco answered, glad to see his friend. Gregoire looked at Shema darkly, as if he might be worried that Shema had overheard his conversation. He knew Shema was Sam's best friend. He slunk off, leaving the two smaller boys together.

"I'm glad you came then," said Bosco, "I thought Gregoire was going to hit me. I told him how the school team hasn't a chance of winning as he can't score goals! If only we had Sam back!" he added with a sigh.

"Well, you might be able to help with that," said Shema.

"How?" enquired Bosco.

"Well," said Shema, "I wondered if Gregoire planted his own ball in Sam's desk to get him into trouble, so he could play in the school team instead. But I needed proof! If you tell what you have heard to Sam's teacher, it may clear Sam's name."

"I don't know," said Bosco tentatively. "Gregoire is such a bully and has already threatened me. He would know that I'd grassed on him."

"I'll come with you," promised Shema. "I overheard what he said. We just have to stand up against a bully, not let him get away with it. Sam's teacher knows me, too, and he knows that I tell the truth."

"OK, if you come with me, then I'll do it," Bosco promised.

So, after school was finished, Shema told Sam to wait for him because he had to see his kind friend, the teacher who had taught him so much before he was able to go to school. Sam was a little surprised to see Bosco going into the classroom with Shema, but waited outside as Shema asked.

"Well, if it isn't my young friend, Shema!" exclaimed the Class Four teacher. "How nice to see you. I hear you are doing very well in Class Two. I see you have a friend with you. What is this all about?"

Shema and Bosco told their story and the teacher listened intently. "Thank you for telling me this," he said. "Go home and for the moment do not say anything to anyone else until I have investigated the matter. Don't worry, I will get to the bottom of it."

The two boys rushed out of the classroom very pleased with themselves. Sam was waiting outside, looking puzzled. "What was that all about?" he asked Shema, after Bosco had started off in the other direction to his home.

"It's a bit of a secret at the moment, so I can't tell you," replied Shema. It was hard not to tell because Sam had suffered so much, but he knew he must obey the teacher. "Come on, race you home!" he said and started running down the dirt path with Sam hard at his heels.

SEVEN

Life in Kigali

Frida was right. She had made a big mistake! The house in which her cousin lived was little more than a hut in a poor area called Muzambi. It was small, dirty and close to many other houses like it. It was noisy, too, with radios blasting out, it seemed, from every house around. Old cars and motor bikes screeched along the dusty road outside, people wandered everywhere and men drank in the bar opposite, all day and all night. Frida hated it. How she longed for the country air, her garden and her clean little house! Most of all she longed for her sister, brother and her dear friend Ishimwe.

Within days of coming to the capital Frida knew her dreams of meeting famous people and becoming a hairdresser would not be coming true. She found herself trapped in her cousin's house, kept like a slave, working from the first light of morning until late at night, cleaning, cooking, washing and looking after the baby. This house had an electric light bulb hanging from the ceiling, so work continued until very late, after which she fell down to sleep on the floor, exhausted.

One thing was true. Justin's wife *was* a very sick lady. She wasn't really old, but she looked like an old lady, very thin and coughing all the time. At first, Frida hated her because she ordered her around; but gradually she began to feel pity for Penina and tried to be kind to her. The only joy was their baby, Manweli. He was just over a year old, but not yet able to walk, so Frida carried him in a cloth on her back while she did the chores. When she had time, she played with him. He was a happy child who soon learnt to put his arms up for Frida to pick him up, and who gave her lovely smiles.

Justin and Penina had very little money, and expected Frida to cook them meals made from almost nothing. Even though Frida was used to struggling to feed her own family, at least in the Village of Hope she was able to grow vegetables and millet in her garden. There was no garden around Justin's house, and food in the small shop near them was much more expensive than in the country. Justin had no regular job but helped on building sites when work was available. What money he did earn was often spent on beer at the bar opposite.

At first, Frida began to think of ways to escape. She considered walking home; even if it took her several days. However, Justin always seemed to be around, watching her. One day he said to her, "Don't try to run away. Everyone in this area knows who you are and will stop you and I will lock you up and beat you to punish you. From now on you will live with us. As your senior relative you must obey me."

After that, Frida was too worried to try to run away. She could not understand how he could be a relative of her kind and loving father. Justin was harsh, selfish and unkind, even to his sick wife. He didn't seem to care about his baby, either, and often shouted at Manweli when he cried.

Penina and Frida gradually became friends. Some days when Penina felt a bit better, they would do the housework together, or at least they would chat. Gradually the house was cleaned up from the terrible mess it had been in. One day when Justin was out and Manweli was asleep, Penina asked Frida to sit with her.

"I need to talk to you while I can," she explained. "I know I am sick and I am sure this sickness will lead to death. I may not have many weeks left to live. Justin's plan is, once I am dead, to take you for his wife. You are young and strong and also very pretty. He will not treat you well for he is a cruel and selfish man. When I die you *must* escape quickly. There is one lady who will help you, and that is my sister. She is called Libertina. For sure, she will attend my funeral. When she comes, do not stay here, but beg her to take you to her home and keep you safe. Try to take Manweli with you, too, for his father will not want him."

This long talk made Penina cough a lot and Frida hurried to get her a drink of water. When she had recovered, Penina thanked Frida for coming and taking care of her. "You have made my last weeks bearable," she said with a sigh.

That night, when all the work was done, Frida lay on the grass mat she used as a mattress and thought about all that Penina had said. She pulled the thin kitenge cloth she used for a blanket around her, and began to cry. Everything seemed so hopeless and her own family so far away.

"If only," she thought, "if only I had not been so selfish and stayed in the Village of Hope! If only I had gone to church that Sunday, then none of this would have happened!"

Frida thought about Ishimwe and how content and happy she was, in spite of her hard life. She knew it had something to do with her loving God as her Father. Ishimwe had tried to tell Frida how much he had helped her, but she had refused to listen, preferring to be angry with God and to hold her bitterness inside herself.

"Could God still really love me, in spite of my anger and all the mistakes I have made?" Frida wondered, as the tears ran down her face. "Oh God, if you really are there please would you forgive me and help me?" she prayed quietly from the depth of her heart. Even though there was noise all around her from the other houses and the bar, Frida felt a quietness come over her, like a blanket of love wrapping her up – and she fell asleep.

The next day everything around her seemed the same, and yet she felt that somehow everything was different. She felt that God had forgiven her, and was with her. She gave Manweli a hug as she washed him, and he laughed, not minding the cold water. Then she took him to Penina to cuddle, and gave her a hug, too. Tears sprang into Penina's eyes.

"No one has hugged me since I became sick, Frida, thank you." Penina said. "Your caring has made such a difference to me." Frida smiled, for the first time for a long time. That day, Frida even found herself singing as she cooked and cleaned. She knew she had at last found God as her Father and that somehow, somehow, he would sort things out for her.

EIGHT

Gregoire and Sam

Sam's teacher was as good as his word. All along he felt an injustice had been done to Sam and now that there seemed to be some evidence he was determined to find out the real story. The day after Bosco and Shema had been to see him, he asked Gregoire to stay behind at break time. He looked very stern and Gregoire was shaking in his shoes. He might be a bully to other children, but, like so many bullies, he wasn't very brave himself!

"Gregoire," said the teacher, "it has come to my attention that you have bragged about getting rid of someone from the school football team. Only one boy has been expelled, and that is Sam. It seems that your red ball didn't get into Sam's desk because Sam had stolen it. What do you have to say for yourself?"

Gregoire went very red and looked at the floor.

"I am waiting for an answer!" said the teacher. "If you do not want to tell me, then maybe you will tell the headmaster?"

At last Gregoire answered. "It was me," he muttered.

"Why did you do such a thing?" questioned the teacher. "It is terrible to accuse someone else of stealing, and Sam has had to endure a very hard punishment. Also the school has suffered because they have lost vital football matches!" The teacher was really angry. Gregoire began to cry a little. "Well?" said the teacher. "I am waiting to hear your reasons!"

"Well sir, I guess I am jealous of Sam. He is always so brilliant at football and I wanted a place in the team. I thought it would please my father if I was in the team. I know what I did was wrong."

"Yes, it was wrong!" exclaimed his teacher. "We teachers are here to help you, and that sometimes means punishing you. I will, of course, report this to the headmaster, for he was informed that Sam had stolen your ball. He will determine your punishment, but first of all, in the next lesson, you will confess to the class about the ball and apologise to Sam."

"Yes sir," said Gregoire, meekly.

After break, when the whole class had settled down at their desks, Gregoire was called to the front. He publicly confessed what he had done, and asked Sam to forgive him.

Sam was amazed. He beamed from ear to ear. God had answered his prayer and had proved Sam was not a thief! Instead of feeling angry, Sam just felt so thankful that it had all been sorted out. Actually, looking at Gregoire, he felt a bit sorry for him. He looked so wretched standing in front of everyone.

"That's all right, Gregoire," he said, "I forgive you. I am glad it is all over." He left his seat and went to the front and shook Gregoire's hand, and smiled at him.

"You don't hate me?" said Gregoire in amazement.

"No, I don't," answered Sam. The class gasped when they heard this, then began to clap. Now it was Sam's turn to feel embarrassed as he returned to his seat.

The teacher smiled at the two boys and then talked to the class about how important it is to both say "sorry", but also to forgive people who have hurt us.

After school the class teacher talked to Sam. He told him how glad he was that the problem had been solved, and he told him that Shema and Bosco had helped to do that. He also said he was very sorry that Sam had been falsely accused and punished.

It was a very happy Sam who ran down the mud path with Shema that afternoon. He wanted to hear the whole story of what Shema and Bosco had done.

"It began with my policeman friend," explained Shema. "He told me the best way to solve such a mystery was to wait and listen very carefully, for eventually someone will boast about what they have done. So I did that. I kept listening to what groups of children were saying, and in the end I did hear Gregoire boasting. It happened to be to Bosco, so I was able to talk to him and we went to see your teacher together. I did keep praying every day that the truth would come out, for I knew you were not the thief!"

Shema ran into his house and shared the good news with Ishimwe and Maji. Janette and Michal were there, too, and they were all so pleased to hear the good news.

"I can't wait to tell the policeman!" said Shema. "It was he who advised me to keep listening and be patient. He told me that many difficult cases are solved that way."

Shema changed out of his school uniform, folded it neatly and put it on his stool. Dressed in his old play clothes he was ready to go to the next village to do his work for the policeman. He sang one of his favourite songs as he went along the path. "God will make a way, where there seems to be no way." God had indeed made a way for Sam's name to be cleared, when there seemed to be no way! He was so thankful, and he knew that Mama Grace and the Old People would be happy, too.

"You look very cheerful today," commented the policeman, as Shema arrived at his house.

"I am, and it's all thanks to you!" replied Shema. "You told me to wait and listen and I did. Then I heard someone bragging about getting a boy kicked out of the football team. I knew it must be Sam, because no one else had been chucked out."

Shema told his friend the whole story before he swept around the garden and weeded among the beans. After he had finished outside he went indoors to see the policeman's wife. She was feeling stronger these days and didn't need much help, but she did have a job for Ishimwe. She wanted her to make a skirt, so asked Shema to take a message. Ishimwe was getting well known as a very good dressmaker!

Shema was just about to leave and run home for supper, when the policeman called him over.

"I have a treat for you and Sam," he said. "I have been asked to go to Ruhengeri, to do a day's work. I have use of the police Land Rover and have asked permission to take you two boys with me, if you are allowed. My work is to be in the volcanoes, where the gorillas live. I have a pass for us to see them. It would mean a *very* early start on Saturday, and we would be late home. I will go and see the social worker at your village and also visit Mama Grace, and if they agree, we will have a great adventure. How do you fancy seeing gorillas?"

Shema was speechless for a moment and went pink with excitement. "Real gorillas? I can't believe it!" he exclaimed. "What an amazing treat! Thank you so much!" and he hugged the policeman.

"I will visit Ishimwe tomorrow, and Sam's mum, and get their permission," said the policeman with a laugh. Then when you come to work, I can tell you the arrangements."

An ecstatic Shema ran all the way home without stopping. He rushed into the house to tell his sister and brother. He was so excited he almost forgot to tell Ishimwe that the policeman's wife wanted to see her about making a skirt. Ishimwe was pleased to hear that news, too! In fact it had been a day of good news, which they all needed.

If only they had some good news about Frida! Ishimwe thought about her friend every day, and asked God to take care of her and bring her home. Somehow, inside herself, Ishimwe knew that Frida had made a bad choice, and worried about what might have happened to her. Janette was coping well and beginning to make some money selling her baskets, which meant they had money for food, but she was missing her sister and missing school, too.

NINE

Auntie Hears Some News

The next day Ishimwe went as usual to Mama Grace's house to make clothes on her sewing machine. It was lovely to see his family so happy again, now that Sam's name had been cleared. Even the Old Lady was singing as she helped Ishimwe cut out her clothes. The policeman had visited Mama Grace early that morning, so everyone was feeling excited about the boys' treat, too.

"My only worry," said Mama Grace, "is that it costs a lot of money to visit the gorillas, but I didn't think to ask how much. Somehow I will have to manage, for it is a chance of a lifetime for them."

Ishimwe hadn't thought about money for the trip. She really didn't know about such things. She had only heard about the gorillas once when they were talked about at school, but that was a very long time ago. "I will ask the policeman's wife when I go to see her later on today about a skirt she wants me to make for her. You are right, we must let the boys have this treat, even if it means using the money I was saving to buy chickens for them as a Christmas surprise!"

Maji and Michal had been having fun helping the Old Man in the garden. They loved being with him and hearing stories of the old days. When the Old Man was a boy, there were many wild animals roaming the countryside. Now they only lived in game reserves, so Maji had never seen an elephant or a zebra. Sometimes monkeys came to steal the ripe corn; if the boys saw them they chased them away. Imagine chasing elephants or zebras away to protect your cows or goats!

Ishimwe and Maji arrived home just before Shema came in from school; they were later than usual because Ishimwe had visited the policeman's wife and measured her for the skirt she wanted her to make. Ishimwe had shyly asked her about the cost of visiting the gorillas. The lady didn't know, but promised to ask her husband.

When they got home they found that Janette was waiting for them. "Guess what!" she said, nearly jumping up and down in excitement. "Auntie Delphine is going all the way to Kigali to make enquiries about Frida!"

"Come and tell me all about it," invited Ishimwe. She should have been starting to cook the beans for supper, but so wanted to hear news of her friend!

Janette was bubbling over with excitement. "At first," she explained, "Auntie had no idea where to begin to look for Frida. Kigali is a very big city. She has made lots of phone calls to talk to people who keep family records. Today she walked to the hill where we used to live, where our family lived for many generations. She asked everyone on that hill if they knew our relatives, and if our father had a cousin called Justin. People remembered our father and mother, our grandparents, our uncles and aunts, but nobody knew a cousin called Justin. The elders in the village talked together and gave Auntie the name of someone from the area who lives in Kigali and might help her. She will travel as soon as she can. I'm so excited! I hope she will get news!"

"Kigali is a long way. Someone should go with her!" exclaimed Ishimwe.

"I will," said Maji, who had been listening to the story.

"It will have to be a grown up, and if possible a man," answered Janette.

"How about the pastor from the church?" suggested Ishimwe, remembering how helpful he had been when they needed a new home. It was he who had helped them get a house in the Village of Hope.

"That's a really good idea," answered Janette. "I will go and talk to Auntie Delphine in the morning and see if she wants someone to go with her."

"I have another good idea," said Ishimwe. "Let's just talk to God about it right now and ask his help, because he knows where Frida is."

So the children held hands and began to talk to their heavenly Father, asking for his help, knowing that he understood.

TEN

Gorillas in the Mist

Sam and Shema were so excited about their trip to see the gorillas in the jungle that they could hardly wait for Saturday to come! Shema was going to sleep at Sam's house because they had to leave at 4 o'clock in the morning. Mama Grace had promised to wake them in time, but even so the boys hardly slept at all. They were afraid of oversleeping and the policeman going without them!

When Ishimwe had asked about the cost, she had been told, much to her amazement, that the boys were to be guests of the Wildlife Centre, since the policeman was going there as part of his job.

It was very dark and cold when Sam and Shema heard the policeman's Land Rover draw up outside the house. Mama Grace made sure the boys were wearing warm sweaters and also gave them a bag of food for breakfast. They were both able to climb into the front, as the vehicle had three front seats, and were soon strapped in. The policeman laughed at the boys' excitement.

They had two hours of travelling and hoped to

arrive at the town of Ruhengeri by first light. "In order to see the gorillas in their natural habitat, you have to start the trek up the mountains early," the policeman told them. The road had many twists and turns, but as it was still dark, there was not much to see, so both boys dozed a little. They woke up when they were nearing the town. Dawn was beginning to break and they could just make out the silhouette of the Virunga volcanoes ahead of them. A few people were beginning to walk along the side of the road, carrying all sorts of things on their heads as they set out for work or to market. It was still cold and the policeman told the boys that they would need their sweaters all day, because it was much colder up in the mountains.

Soon they pulled into a yard and their friend told them that they were at the head office of the Gorilla Protection Department. Over the gate was an arch, which held a model of a huge gorilla, much bigger even than the policeman! The boys gasped in amazement. "Are they really that big?" asked Shema.

"The mature males, called silverbacks, are that size," the policeman answered. "But don't worry, you will be safe with the wardens and trackers!"

They went into the building and had to sign their names in a book before they were given their permits. It made the boys feel very important! Then they were transferred to a special safari vehicle and they sat each side of the policeman. Apart from the three of them and the driver, all the other passengers were white people, "Muzungus" as they were called in the Kinyarwanda language.

By this time it was quite light and the boys were excited to see everything around them. They travelled north for about 20 minutes before arriving at the Visitor Centre, where they met all the other tourists who would be trekking up the mountains with them, hoping to see gorillas. They were all told how to behave; they mustn't make any sudden noises or movements and they must not cough or sneeze, because gorillas can catch human diseases and die from them. They must listen to instructions from their warden and guide at all times, who would tell them how close they could go to the animals. Then, they all got into another Land Rover and drove as far as they could into the mountain. When the track stopped, everyone got out and they began to trek. At first the walk was easy, but as they climbed higher the boys found they were getting a little breathless. It was very cold, too, and at times they walked through a wet mist.

The boys had never seen thick forest like this! The policeman explained that many of the trees were bamboo, which the gorillas loved to eat. With them was a guide who had a walkie-talkie. Other guides who had been on the mountain all night told him where to go to find the animals. The group also had a soldier with them, carrying a gun, which frightened

Shema at first, but his policeman friend reassured him. The soldier was there for their protection just in case an animal behaved badly. It was a government regulation, but it was very unlikely that there would be any trouble.

It was cold and drizzling in the forest, making the boys shiver a little. How glad they were to have their sweaters! They trekked behind the guide, winding through the bamboo forest, climbing higher and higher. Some of the older people in the party were finding it hard work, so every now and then the guide had to stop for them to catch up.

"Be very quiet now and only talk in whispers," the guide suddenly told them. "We are very near the gorillas." He began to make a strange noise, as if talking in gorilla language, to warn the gorillas that they were around. He wanted the animals to remain calm and not to start racing to another location. The party stopped at a small clearing. They were warned not to go any closer when they saw the gorillas, and to be careful how they took photographs. If they pointed the camera straight at a gorilla's eyes, he might feel threatened and become angry, and he wouldn't like flash photography either! Of course, that was no problem for Shema and Sam as they didn't have a camera.

After standing still in the clearing for a few minutes, Shema suddenly gasped in surprise as a gorilla family walked right out into the clearing, just a few metres away! There was a large male with his silver back, a mother carrying her tiny baby and about six other gorillas of various sizes. At first the boys were a bit scared, but gradually they lost their fear and just looked at the animals in amazement. Most of the white people were taking photos. One young man spoke to the boys and asked them a question, but of course, they could not understand what he was saying, because he spoke a foreign language. The guide came over.

"This man would like to take pictures of you with the gorillas in the background," he explained.

"OK," the boys agreed. A few minutes after the photo was taken, they heard a strange noise in the camera, and out came a photo. They were so surprised! They could see themselves and the gorillas!

When the young man saw how excited the boys were, he took two more photographs and when they were ready he gave one to Shema and the other to Sam. The boys had never had their photos taken before, let alone possessed a photo. They were so thrilled with the gift that the guide had to remind them not to make too much noise! They tried to remember the little English and French they knew. Sam said "Thank you very much", while Shema managed "Merci beaucoup" quite well. The young man smiled back at them.

The group stayed on the mountain watching the gorillas for about an hour. Then the party began to trek back down the mountain. They seemed to get down a lot quicker than it had taken them to climb up! Once down the mountain, they found the sun was out and it was warmer. Even so, it was still only half past eleven. They drove back to the Visitor Centre and were each given a certificate to show that they had been on a gorilla safari. It had a picture on it of the family they had seen. Shema thought how he could pin it on the wall of their house and everyone would be able to see the mountain gorillas! The certificate said they had visited Family Group Thirteen. They even had the names of the gorillas and their photos on the back! What a treasure; the boys felt as rich as kings!

The policeman now had to go to a meeting. He had been asked to teach the soldiers how to capture poachers who were trying to kill the gorillas. Meanwhile the boys were told to stay at the Visitor Centre with the guide. They were given a delicious lunch, which they ate up quickly as their safari had made them very hungry! The guide told them many interesting facts about gorillas, while they were eating. He told them, too, that they could help with the protection of these wonderful animals by telling the other children at their school all they had learnt. "The young generation need to grow up and respect the wonderful wildlife of Rwanda," he explained.

"We certainly will tell everyone about our wonderful

trip here. It's terrible that the gorillas are in danger from poachers," said Sam.

Shema nodded in agreement. "We will never forget the gorillas. How could anyone kill such magnificent creatures?"

When their friend had finished his meeting, they all climbed into the Land Rover and began the journey home. This time it was daylight and they could see the countryside and how the road twisted and turned through the hills. It was not a mud road, but black tarmac. The boys were amazed even by this!

"How did people make a road like this, cutting through the hills?" Sam asked.

"It was very difficult," the policeman told him. "Many people died making this road. They were not our people, but had come from a land far away, called China. Some died because they were not used to our climate and food. Others caught malaria and it killed them. On the way home I will show you the place where they are buried. They have their own burial ground, according to their culture," he added. "I will also point out to you a big waterfall. There is much good water here and some of it is bottled for people to drink, like the white people you met today. They need to drink very pure water if they are to keep well in our country. We also have to boil our water to kill any germs, but you know that. Never drink water straight from a stream or a well or you might get sick."

"We are careful," replied Shema, thinking how Ishimwe boiled water for them every day.

"By the way, I am not sure, but I think that I may have some good news for you," remarked the policeman. "You know, Shema, that I have told you before that it is very important to listen carefully to people because you may get a vital clue about a crime that has been committed. Well, that has happened to me today! Some of the men at my lecture were talking together as we drank tea. They were discussing some of the bad things which happen in our country, not just poaching gorillas, but other things, too. One man mentioned that he had heard about a scandal that was happening in an area of Kigali called Muzambi. Some men are pretending to be related to children with no parents, and taking them into their families where they make them work hard for no pay. When I heard this I asked some questions, as it is possible that this may be what has happened to your friend, Frida. I will see your social worker, Delphine, as soon as we get back."

The boys were excited when they heard this news. Maybe Frida could be found – that would be the perfect end to the most wonderful day of their lives!

Eventually they left the good road and turned on to the dusty red track. "We will soon be home," their friend told them.

Although it had been an incredible adventure, Shema and Sam were very glad to be home. They were so tired! They proudly showed everyone their certificates and photos. They would never forget that incredible adventure as long as they lived!

ELEVEN

Penina Becomes Very Sick

Ever since the night Frida had asked God to forgive her and be her Father, she had found that she was able to do her work without feeling angry and bitter. She still hated living in the city and being treated like a slave, though, and as she saw Penina grow weaker, she became more and more afraid for her own future. What would happen when Penina died? Would she really have to marry Justin? The thought was too awful to think about.

Frida tried not to think too much about the future and devoted herself to taking care of Penina and little Manweli. She kept out of Justin's way as much as possible, hating it when he came home after a bout of drinking alcohol in the bar. More and more Frida found herself talking to her Father God about her fears and worries. She usually felt calmer after these times and although she didn't hear a voice out loud, inside she felt God whispering to her, "I will take care of you." Sometimes she heard Christian songs and messages coming from a radio in a neighbour's house, which she found comforting. Still, her thoughts constantly turned to Hope Village and her sister and brother, and she wished with all her heart that she had never left them.

Very early one morning she woke up with a start. Justin was shaking her arm. "Penina is calling for you," he said. "I don't think she has long to live."

Frida quickly ran to Penina, who seemed to be weaker than ever. Between spasms of coughing she asked Frida to take Manweli and fetch her sister. She pushed a piece of paper in the girl's hand, with her sister's address written on it.

"Go, go," she said. Frida gave the sick woman a kiss and covered her with her blanket. She turned and picked up Manweli and tied him on her back, clutching the paper in her hand. She was leaving the house when Justin confronted her.

"Where do you think you are going?" he demanded.

Frida looked at him, suddenly unafraid. "I am fetching Penina's sister," she answered. "Your wife is very sick and needs her." For a moment Frida thought that Justin was going to stop her, then suddenly he turned, put his hand in his pocket and pulled out some money.

"You will need this," he said. "Take the bus to Kicukiro market and ask for Libertina at the pineapple stand; you will find her there." Then he sneered in a very unpleasant way. "Come back at once, or I will send my friends out to find you," he added.

"I will," replied Frida, amazed at how calm she felt. "Thank you for the bus fare," she added as she began to walk along the path towards the road where the bus stopped.

Once away from Justin's shack her legs began to tremble a little. She had hardly been outside since she left the Village of Hope so many weeks ago, except to the well to fetch water and the local shops for food. In her hand was the crumpled piece of paper. In her spidery handwriting Penina had managed to write, "Libertina, Kicukiro market."

"Please help me to find Penina's sister," Frida prayed. "Help me to find the right bus, as well," she added, feeling overwhelmed by the busy, noisy road and rushing traffic.

At the bus stop people were beginning to gather; children were making their way to school and grown ups to work. A lady with a huge basket on her head waited beside Frida at the bus stop.

"Are you going to market Mama?" Frida asked politely. "Yes, my dear," she answered, "I have many eggs to sell at Kicukiro today."

"Kicukiro!" exclaimed Frida in delight. "That is where I am going, too. May I travel with you?"

"Of course my dear," said the lady kindly. "Is that your lovely baby on your back?"

"Oh no!" answered Frida, "Manweli is not mine! He is the son of my cousin, but I have to go to the market and find his aunt."

Soon the bus came, and there was a lot of pushing and shoving as people piled into it; far more people than it was ever made to carry! How glad Frida was to follow the lady with the basket! From her she learnt the correct fare, and they stood squashed together in the aisle as there was no room to sit. It was such a comfort not to feel totally alone in this crowd of strangers. After about 20 minutes they arrived. By this time Frida was feeling a bit sick, for she had not eaten any breakfast. Manweli was crying, too.

"Do you know where to find this child's aunt?" asked the lady with the basket of eggs, as Frida stepped gratefully off the bus behind her and looked around.

"She will be selling pineapples," replied Frida, "and her name is Libertina."

"I do not know that name," answered the kind lady, "but come with me. The person from whom I rent my stall will know. He knows everybody!"

Frida duly followed her new friend, aware that her Father God had brought this lady along her way to help her! Sure enough, the stall owner knew exactly where to find Penina's sister. That was such a help because the market was the biggest Frida had ever seen. Just looking around made her feel a bit dizzy!

The stall owner pointed out where to go and Frida followed his instructions carefully. When she found the pineapple stall she shyly explained to the lady who she was, and showed her the piece of paper.

Frida was relieved to find that the lady was Libertina herself! Libertina was shocked to hear the news that her sister was so very sick. She looked at Frida a little suspiciously at first. "Who are you and how come you are staying with my sister?" she asked.

Frida told Libertina the whole story, then explained that the little boy on her back was Penina's son. Libertina gave the little boy a cuddle, while brushing tears from her eyes.

"My darling little nephew," she crooned, then turned to Frida. "Come, I will take you both to my house and you shall both have a proper breakfast while I tell my family that I'm going back to Penina's house with you. I'll need to pack a few things, in case I stay for a while, even though I don't like her husband."

Fortunately Libertina's home was close to the market. It was quite the most beautiful house Frida had ever been in, with several rooms and exquisite fabrics decorating elegant furniture. After a quick breakfast, Libertina's husband drove them straight back to Justin and Penina's house in Muzambi, where they found Penina lying in her bed, almost too weak to sit up, but so glad to see her sister.

TWELVE

Frida's Rescue

In the Village of Hope, the social worker, Delphine, had made several phone calls to the capital city, trying to find out what might have happened to Frida – but with no success. She had already been to Kigali once, to search through Frida's official family records, but there was no trace of anyone called Justin. She felt convinced this man must be an imposter! Now that the policeman had told her orphans were being tricked into leaving their homes to become forced servants in Muzambi, she had a much stronger lead to follow up. The policeman advised her not to travel alone, so when the children suggested the pastor might go with her, she jumped at the idea.

On the day of the journey, the pastor's wife decided to spend the day in Hope Village while Delphine was away with the pastor, looking for Frida. The pastor didn't know much about the city, but was a big, strong man who cared very much for children in need, and Delphine felt much safer going to search for Frida in Kigali with him by her side.

They walked along the dry mud road for about an

hour, then picked up a taxi-bus that was going to Kigali. It took another hour or so for them to arrive in the city. They walked up and down the lines of buses in the bus station and eventually found one which was marked "Muzambi". Soon they were winding up a hill, once again on a red earth road, until the bus stopped at its destination. The pastor and Delphine got out and looked around them. "Wherever do we start looking?" Delphine wondered.

"I think we should just stop and ask the Lord God to show us what to do and where to go," answered the pastor. After a simple prayer for help, right there in the street, the pastor suggested that they visit the nearest shop, which sold milk. Many people were going in and out with little plastic bottles for their milk, so Delphine and the pastor crossed the road and joined the queue.

"Why, you have no container!" one lady said to them. "You need a container to get milk."

"We have not come to buy milk," Delphine explained, "we have come to ask questions because we are trying to find a young friend who we think might be living in Muzambi." The pastor then explained that they were looking for a 13-year-old girl called Frida who was living with her cousin, Justin, and his wife. The customers began to ask each other if they knew such a person.

"I think I may know who you mean," the milk seller said. "Sometimes a young girl comes in, usually with a baby boy on her back. I believe her name is Frida. She came to live with her cousin and his wife a few weeks ago. The wife is very sick; indeed I believe she is dying."

"That lady died, yesterday," one of the customers added. "The husband's name is Justin, so that must be the girl you are looking for! The wife is due to be buried at noon, so if you hurry to the house, you might be in time."

"Do you know where they live?" the pastor asked. "The girl you mentioned, Frida – she must be the girl we are looking for. We really need to find her!"

After taking directions from the helpful people in the shop, Delphine and the pastor almost ran to the house.

They found it without any trouble and were disturbed to find that it was a very poor shack. "Poor Frida, living here," murmured Delphine, with a tear in her eye. There was nobody in, but some kind neighbours invited them in.

"The family will soon be back from the cemetery," they assured the pastor and Delphine, assuming they had come for the funeral. "Would you like a cup of tea while you wait?"

The pastor and Delphine gladly accepted the offer and while they were drinking, explained who they were and why they were looking for Frida.

"Why, yes!" the neighbour exclaimed, "a girl called Frida does live here! She came to help the family a few weeks ago; she must be the girl you are seeking. I do not know what Penina would have done without her because Justin is a bad man. Frida has worked day and night and been treated by him like a slave! We've heard him boasting when he's been drinking that he will take her as his wife once Penina is dead!"

Pastor and Delphine looked at each other in alarm when they heard this. They simply had to rescue Frida! Just then they heard a commotion next door and realised that the family must have returned from the cemetery.

The pastor knew he had to act quickly in order to rescue Frida. Leaving Delphine at the neighbour's house he decided to visit Justin. Just as he was praying for the right words and right approach, he heard a man's voice.

"Go and fetch water for tea," the man said roughly, and the pastor saw Frida run out of the house with a jerry can! "Frida!" he called quietly. She turned round, startled, and then a smile crept over her tear-stained face as she recognised Ishimwe's pastor.

"Don't be afraid," he said, "Auntie Delphine and I are here to try and help you. Do you want to return home to Hope Village?"

"Oh yes! More than I can ever say," she responded, "but my cousin Justin will never let me. He says I must marry him now that Penina, his wife has died. It was so terrible to see her die!" Tears started to stream down Frida's face again as she gently patted the sleeping baby on her back. "Anyway, if I leave, what will happen to little Manweli?"

"Dear child," replied the pastor kindly, "God will make a way!"

Leaving Frida to fetch the water, the pastor boldly went to the front of the shack, called out a traditional greeting and walked in.

Justin looked up. "Who are you?" he asked.

"I am a pastor and have come to offer sympathy and pray with you at this sad time," he answered.

Justin looked a little uncomfortable. "I do not pray," he said, but he did not want to appear rude, so asked his guest to stay and take tea.

"Thank you," said the pastor, sitting on the bench next to a lady, who introduced herself as Penina's sister, Libertina.

"Thank you for coming, Pastor," she said, then when Justin was busy chatting to some other guests, she quietly confided in the pastor that she was concerned for her baby nephew and also for Frida.

The pastor then explained the real reason for his visit. Libertina pursed her lips grimly when she heard that Justin had tricked Frida into coming and working for him as a home help with no pay. "I will help you," she promised. "If you take the girl home, I will gladly take little Manweli and bring him up as my own son."

Encouraged by these words, the pastor greeted Frida in front of all the people gathered there. "Frida, my dear," he said, "you have done your duty well in caring for Penina. Now you can return with me and Auntie Delphine to the Village of Hope to care for your own sister and brother. They need you, too! If you want to come home with us tonight, then gather your things together now. We leave shortly!"

"You can't take her away!" shouted Justin. "She is my cousin and so I have parental rights over her. I want to marry her!"

"Who says she is your cousin?" asked the pastor. "Unless you have documentation to prove you are the cousin of this girl's father, then you have no claim! Frida is still a child, anyway, so you cannot marry her!"

Justin, like the coward he was, crumbled when he was faced with the truth. He admitted that he had enticed Frida into his home under false pretences and had paid her nothing.

Libertina was so angry, she took charge. "You will give the girl money now!" she demanded, "and let her go in peace!"

Justin put his hand in his pocket and took out a wad of notes. He counted some out and handed the money to Frida. "But what will happen to my son without Frida to look after him?" he whined. "I can't look after him myself!"

Libertina scowled at him. "He is my nephew and I will take him into my family. He will be raised well. We will do it to honour our sister Penina." Libertina turned to face all the other relatives gathered for the funeral. "You are all witnesses to what has happened here today, that Frida is freed and Manweli protected."

Frida smiled at Libertina, then at the pastor. "I'll get my things," she said and went behind the rough curtain that hung between the two rooms to gather her few belongings and tie them in a cloth. She had handed Manweli to Libertina after giving him one last hug and kiss. She felt sad to say goodbye to him, but was glad that he would be brought up in a good home.

"You will always be welcome in our home to visit him, my dear. Thank you for your love and care for him and for my dear sister, Penina," said Libertina.

At last Frida's ordeal was over! The pastor called next door to collect Delphine, who gave Frida a great big hug, and the three of them began their journey back to the Village of Hope.

THIRTEEN

Home Again

It was getting late by the time Pastor, Delphine and Frida left Muzambi. The pastor decided they should stay that night in the city, then start early in the morning for their village. They were all tired and hungry. They caught a taxi-bus into the middle of the city and found a guest house with rooms that were clean and comfortable. Frida shared a room with Delphine, for she was still frightened and did not want to be alone. The owners of the guest house were very helpful and told them where they could buy food at a good price. The meal seemed like a feast to Frida! She was expecting to be told off and punished because she had run away, but all she received was love and kindness. She was amazed!

* * *

Back in the Village of Hope, the pastor's wife was keeping an eye on Janette and Michal. She knew the children a little because they had been attending the church with Ishimwe and her family. When Janette showed her the baskets which she was weaving, she was truly amazed at the skill such a young girl had acquired.

"Are they selling well in the market?" she asked.

"Quite well, thank you," Janette answered. "I am grateful to Ishimwe who takes them there each week and puts them on her stall to sell with her clothes."

"I think I could sell some, too, to ladies in the church. They are so nicely made!" the pastor's wife commented.

"That would be so good!" Janette smiled. "The extra money will help Frida with the housekeeping when she comes home!"

"Well, that's settled then. You make me six to start with and we will see how we get on! Now how about your evening meal?" She was very sad when she saw how little food there was. There was only enough for a small meal of rice and beans. After they had eaten, Ishimwe, Shema and Maji came over to chat.

Ishimwe said what they were all thinking. "I wonder if Delphine and the pastor have found Frida yet?"

"I don't know," replied the pastor's wife, "but I doubt they will come home tonight. It is already getting dark. I think we should all pray together and then go to bed. I must get home to my family for the night, too. In the morning I'll ask the shopkeeper if he has any news. As they have the only phone in the village, Delphine might phone and leave a message for us there."

The children all prayed together, asking their Father God to help the search for Frida so that she would come home quickly. They didn't know that Frida had already been rescued!

After they had prayed Shema had an idea. "Why don't we plan a party to welcome Frida home!" he suggested. "You know, like the story in the Bible when the runaway son came back. You remember the story, don't you Michal?" he asked his friend. "We heard it in Sunday School. The son ran away to have lots of fun in the big city, but when his money was all gone he was so hungry he decided to go home and say sorry to his dad. When he got back they had a big party because the dad was so pleased that his son was back safe!"

"Yes, that is a wonderful Bible story. We certainly could prepare a party when we know Frida is on her way home," said the pastor's wife.

"I could buy some treats in the market tomorrow!" said Ishimwe enthusiastically.

"I could dig up some of my sweet potatoes in the morning!" added Shema.

"I'll make the best meal I can!" nodded Janette, and Michal and Maji ran around in excitement.

"Be careful not to get too excited," the pastor's wife warned the children. "We must not assume that Frida has been found." But the children didn't listen – they carried on planning happily. As the pastor's wife walked home she prayed for her husband and Delphine, that they would be successful in their mission. She did not want it all to end in disappointment.

* * *

Delphine listened to some of Frida's story before they went to sleep, and was so thankful that they had rescued the girl before anything worse happened to her. She decided they had to do some shopping before they went home. Frida needed a dress or two as her clothes were now looking really worn, so they went to the shops as soon as they opened and Delphine bought her a lovely red patterned dress and a new kitenge cloth to go with it. Frida was so excited! It made her feel really special! Then, the three of them set off for the bus station to start their journey home, but not before they had eaten some breakfast and thanked God for his help. Frida told the pastor how she had prayed in her despair and asked for God's forgiveness. He encouraged her to believe that now she was a child in God's family.

"The Lord promises to answer all who call out to him and no one who comes to him will be turned away. We are promised this in God's book, the Bible," he added.

Back in the village, before he went to school, Shema went to his vegetable plot and dug up some sweet potatoes which he had been growing for a special occasion. Surely, nothing could be more special than

Frida coming home! He had no doubt at all that Delphine and the pastor would find her. After all, Jesus knew where all of them were every moment of every day! He ran into the house and gave his sweet potatoes to Ishimwe, then changed into his uniform and ran off to meet Sam for school. Sam's mum, Mama Grace, was waiting with him.

"Is there any news yet of Frida?" she asked.

"Not yet," replied Sam, "but we are sure that she will be found and come home. When she does, we're going to have a party to welcome her back! I have dug my sweet potatoes ready for the feast!"

Mama Grace smiled at Shema's excitement. "I do hope you are right, Shema. We must continue to pray."

Janette was up early that morning, too. She sent Michal to the well to get more water than usual and cleaned the little house from top to bottom. By the time the pastor's wife arrived she had almost finished!

"Wonderful news!" said a rather breathless pastor's wife, who had been walking as fast as she could. "My husband had been able to telephone the village shopkeeper. Frida is safe and well and they are coming home this morning!"

Janette danced a little jig of joy, then gave the woman a hug! "Oh thank you, thank you! I am so happy!"

"Don't thank me," replied the pastor's wife. "It's God we must thank."

"Of course!" said Janette, and she called to Michal to tell him and the three of them thanked God for the wonderful news.

"Now, we must plan that party!" said the pastor's wife.

"I have already got some nice food," said Janette excitedly. "Shema dug his sweet potatoes, and Ishimwe brought me some peanuts. She is also getting some treats when she is in the market!"

The pastor's wife and Janette sang as they began to prepare the feast. Michal and Maji prepared a surprise of their own. First they ran to tell Mama Grace and the Old People the good news that Frida had been found. Then they bought a pink toilet roll, rushed back and draped it like a paper chain around the living room! They thought it looked wonderful! As Frida still wasn't back, they went out again to pick wild flowers, which they put into an old plastic water bottle for a vase.

Ishimwe had a good morning at the market, but her mind was more on Frida than on selling her clothes and Janette's baskets. At noon she decided to go home. She couldn't decide whether to buy cakes for a party or not, so she discussed it with the lady on the stand next to hers.

"If your friend doesn't come home today, what will you do with them?" asked the lady. "They will go stale!"

Ishimwe suddenly decided. "I have such a light

heart, I feel somehow that all is well and I think she will get home."

The lady nodded and smiled. "Well buy the cakes then, child. I look forward to hearing about the party next week!"

When she reached the Village of Hope, carrying her precious load of delicious-looking cakes and rolls, she heard that their prayers had been answered; the whole village was buzzing with excitement! The children and the pastor's wife were singing as they prepared the party food, and Sam and Shema had run home from school to help. Mama Grace had come with a chicken stew and stayed, too. Everyone was so thrilled to hear that Frida was on her way home!

It was a very large, excited group who ran to meet Frida, the pastor and Delphine as they turned into the village! "Welcome home!" Janette greeted her big sister, with a hug and tears in her eyes. "Welcome home! We have a party for you!"

Frida kept trying to say how sorry she was for all the trouble she had caused, but everyone was just so pleased to have her home again, safe and sound!

Shema told her that it was a Bible story that had given him the idea of a "welcome home" party. Frida had never heard the story so she asked Shema to tell it to her. At the end, he explained that the father in the story is like Father God, and we are like the boy who wanted to go his own way, but God loves us so much that he is longing for us to come home to him.

When we do, there is a big party in heaven, because God is so happy! Frida thought for a few minutes, trying to take in the wonderful story.

"There was a party for me in heaven, then, Shema," she said, "because when I was in Kigali I asked God to forgive me for all the mess I had made of my life and I asked him to be my Father."

Shema was so happy when he heard this news. "You must tell Ishy," he said. "She will be so pleased; it's even better than hearing you were coming home!"

FOURTEEN

The Semi-finals

After all the excitement of Frida's return, Sam and Shema had to work very hard at school as it was nearing the end of term and there were class exams to sit. It was hard to concentrate because it was the middle of the hot, dry season and dust was flying everywhere. The children longed for the rains to come and for it to be a little cooler. It seemed too hot even to play football, but there were several important matches for the school team to play, so they had to keep practising! Now that Sam was back in the team, and reinstated as the captain, they were managing to win lots of the matches and had real hopes of getting into the schools' final.

Shema had done very well in his first term at school, but he also wanted to do well in the exams. It would bring him one step nearer to fulfilling his dream of being an airline pilot. He wanted to please Mrs Mugisha, too, and also the Class Four teacher who had taught him before he was able to go to school and who had so much faith in him.

The term was due to end just before Christmas and

then there was the long six week holiday to enjoy. Sam's sister Grace was coming home from boarding school, and everyone was looking forward to seeing her again, especially her family.

Most of the vegetables in the garden had dried up, due to the heat, and fresh food was quite scarce. One day, on the way home from school Sam had a good idea.

"Let's drum for ants and take them home for supper!" he suggested. "I can use my plastic water bottle."

"Great idea!" Shema nodded in agreement. They went near an ant hill and placed their bottles, with the lids off, into the ground and began to play them gently, like drums. The noise sounded so much like rain falling that it tricked the ants into coming up out of the ground and the boys caught them in the bottles. It was an age-old trick, and it worked very well! The ants were big, fat and juicy. They sometimes stung the boys as they handled them, but that was a small price to pay for such good food! Taken home and fried in a little palm oil, they were a very special treat. Indeed, when the boys arrived home that day with the ants no one minded they were a little late because of the treat they brought with them. They tasted like crispy bacon and everyone loved them!

Just before the end of term, the headmaster announced that the school football team would be playing the semi-final match at home. Everyone cheered. They were so glad they could watch and support their own team! The opposing team was from a different sector, and they were known to be very good. Shema helped Sam train by feeding him balls whenever they had free time to play.

Most of the children wanted to watch the match, and were delighted when the headmaster informed them that the game would be played in school time and all lessons would be cancelled! There was great excitement. Shema plucked up courage to ask the headmaster if Maji and Michal could come and watch. The head answered that they were very welcome, as were any of the children in the Village of Hope. "The more the merrier!" he said with a smile.

On the day of the match, two very old buses drove up to the school in a cloud of dust. The opposing team and their supporters had arrived! The team were given cool drinks and a snack before they went to change into their kit. Like the home team, most of them were from poor families and none of them had proper football boots, but didn't mind a bit; they were used to playing in bare feet or plastic shoes. A referee and linesmen had come from the capital city; they looked very important and smart.

All the supporters sat by the pitch. Not only did Maji and Michal arrive to support the school team, but so did Ishimwe, Janette, Frida and a whole crowd of children from the Village of Hope. A little way behind them puffing because of the heat, came Mama

Grace. She wanted to see her son play – she was so proud of him!

Indeed, they were all very proud of Sam as he led his team on to the pitch. It turned out to be an exciting match! The visiting school opened the scoring with a wonderful goal that no goalkeeper would have been able to stop! Everyone cheered, even those supporting the home team, but they were not so enthusiastic when a second goal was scored just before half time. A rather dispirited home team gathered around Sam while they had their drinks during the break.

"We must not get discouraged," he assured them. "We are a very good team. Let us play as a team, keep passing cleanly and we will get our opportunities. We must work together and do our very best. Today, we are putting our little village on the map of Rwanda!"

The teams went out for the second half. It seemed that Sam's team had renewed energy, while the other team perhaps felt they had already won and relaxed a little. After ten minutes one of the forwards saw an opportunity and slid the ball past the goalkeeper into the net. The home team's supporters shouted and clapped! A few minutes later, Sam had a glorious opportunity and headed a great equaliser. 2-2! This time, the noise was so great that probably the cheers could have been heard all the way down to the Village of Hope! The second goal stung the visiting team into action again and after that the play was fast and furious. Then, one of the visiting team's defenders fouled a home player in the penalty box. It was a penalty! You could have heard a pin drop as Sam went to take the spot kick. Shema closed his eyes and prayed, "Please don't let him miss!"

Sam struck the ball straight and true, into the bottom corner of the net! The supporters yelled and cheered and danced around making so much noise that they could hardly hear the final whistle when it came! They had won! The home team would be in the finals in Kigali!

Mama Grace was crying with joy and Ishimwe and Frida began a traditional dance to celebrate. Soon many others joined in and showed their appreciation of the team by dancing for them. Someone had fetched the school drum and was beating the time for the dance. Everyone was celebrating! The visitors were very sporting and clapped the team as they walked off the pitch to change. There didn't have showers or changing rooms, but the boys put on their school uniforms again and for a special treat the headmaster had arranged for some passion fruit juice to be made and little doughnuts to be cooked for the players of both teams. Then the visitors piled in their buses and everyone waved them off as they drove away in a cloud of dust.

The next day the head announced that the finals would be played just before school closed for the long holiday. He had arranged for a bus to take the team to the capital city, and another bus for parents and friends. Each child in the team could take two guests, either their parents or friends. Shema and Sam ran back to Sam's house at top speed when school had finished for the day. Still panting, Sam asked his mother, "Please will you come, and may Shema come, too?"

"Of course, I wouldn't miss it and I am sure Shema wouldn't either!" Mama Grace replied. Shema was almost crying with joy! He couldn't think of anything more wonderful than supporting his best friend at the final in Kigali!

FIFTEEN

Delphine's Good Idea

Frida had quickly settled back into village life. Janette had not returned to school as it was so near the end of term, so the two girls tackled the housework, cooking and gardening together. In their spare time Janette taught her sister how to weave baskets. These baskets were selling well in the market, and, true to her word, the pastor's wife managed to sell some to the women in the church. Frida now went along to church every week with Ishimwe and all the younger children. When she had called upon God to help her in Kigali and also asked him to forgive all the things she had done wrong, she knew that a change had taken place in her life. She began to feel happier and was beginning to understand, through the teaching of the Bible, that she also needed to forgive her enemies, even the people who had killed her parents.

She was struggling to do that, but was willing to try. Her nightmares came less often now, and when she did have them, she would pray to Jesus when she woke up. Ishimwe continued to be her best friend and they still loved to skip and talk together when all the work was finished. Frida often talked about Manweli, the little boy whom she had grown to love so dearly. Together the girls would pray and ask God to take care of him and keep him safe.

* * *

Auntie Delphine had been troubled about the safety of the children in the Village of Hope since Frida had run away. A few days after the homecoming party, on a Saturday morning, Delphine called a meeting for all the children in the village. She explained to them the dangers of trusting strangers, even if they said they were family. She made every child promise that they would always talk to her about their problems and told them all that even if it was a Sunday and her day off, they must still come and find her if they needed to, and must never go away with strangers.

Delphine loved her work overseeing the Village of Hope. Every time a new sponsor was found to help with a child's education, she became really excited. One or two of the children had now gone to secondary school and were doing well. That was her dream for all the children, that they should do well! They had all endured so much sadness in their young lives and Delphine wanted them now to have happiness. Frida running away had made her realise how very hard it was for the older children in the village who had the responsibility of parenting their younger sisters and brothers. They made such a big sacrifice by not completing their own education. They had no real way to learn skills or get jobs themselves. In fact, although they were in nice houses and a safe environment, they had no opportunity to use their own talents.

Delphine could think of no practical way of helping the older children get more education. Then she thought about the pastor and his wife from the next village who had helped her find Frida. "Maybe they might have some ideas," she thought to herself. "I'll go and visit them!"

The pastor and his wife were very pleased to see Delphine. They respected her work as the social worker for the children. "Come in, come in," said the pastor's wife. "It is so good to see you. Is all well with the children?"

"Yes, thank you, all is well," answered Delphine, "but I want your advice."

"Tell us your problem," said the Pastor, "and we will try to help."

Delphine explained the worry that she felt for the older children who had little education and how she wanted to help them get skills which would give them a future. The pastor and his wife listened carefully, nodding their heads from time to time.

"Let us ask God for some good ideas," suggested the pastor. Quietly they said a prayer together, then sat thinking.

"Well," said the pastor, "I think we need two things.

Number One, we need classes for the older children so that they can learn the basics of numeracy and literacy, and Number Two, we need classes where they can learn basic skills like carpentry, needlework, basketry, car mechanics and things like that."

"But how could we ever do that?" asked Delphine. "We can't send them to school. Very few of the older children get sponsored and usually only one child in each family can be sponsored as there are so many children who need help."

"I think we could do it," said the pastor thoughtfully. "First, we would need a schoolroom. That could be Project Number One. We would have to wait until the rains, then teach the children how to make mud bricks, dry them, and then construct a building. Some of the boys would love to do that! It might be a problem to afford iron sheets for the roof, but in time we could save up for that. Once the walls are up we come to Project Number Two. They learn to cut the right trees, saw them for planks and make benches. This way they learn carpentry skills. Project Number Three could be gathering and drying the long grasses from beside the river and weaving them into mats for the floor!"

Delphine nodded, a glimmer of excitement in her eyes. "But who would teach them all these skills?"

"Lots of people in the church have different skills; most would be pleased to be involved in helping," assured the pastor.

His wife nodded in agreement. "When we have this

basic building, then for an hour or so each day I will happily come and teach reading. I am sure there will be someone in the village who could teach maths and other skills – Mama Grace has taught Ishimwe to sew, I am sure she will teach others. I know people who can bake, who can weave, and there must be men who can help with mechanical skills."

"Well, I think we have some very good ideas," said her husband. "Delphine, what do you think?"

Delphine nodded cheerfully. "I think it could work, and be a solution to the problem," she said. "I will need to talk to the charity that built the village, and also the local authority, to gain permission to build a school on the land. We still have a month or so left of the dry season, so it gives me time to get permission. The first thing I will do is to call a meeting of the whole Village of Hope and put it to the children. I think they will be pleased!"

The more the three thought about it, the better the idea seemed. The pastor promised to call a meeting for the people of his church and their village to see who would be willing to help teach the young people. "I think we need to give it a name. We can't use 'school' because we will not be registered or have exams or qualifications," said Delphine

"How about Hope Skills Centre?" suggested the pastor.

"That is very good," agreed both women.

So the Hope Skills Centre was born!

SIXTEEN

The Football Final

Two days before school ended for the Christmas holiday, the trip to Kigali for the football final took place. Hardly anyone, either in the team or in the supporters' bus, had ever been to the capital city before, so there was a huge buzz of excitement.

Some of the mothers had carefully washed and ironed the school's strip, so that the boys would look as smart as they possibly could. One father, who was a shopkeeper, had given each child a pair of trainers. Not the expensive kind with a brand logo on them, but even so, it was an amazingly generous gift. Most of the children had only ever owned a pair of plastic flip-flops, so to have a pair of real trainers was wonderful! The school had been given some football socks years before, along with the strip, but as the boys played in bare feet, the socks had, until now, just lived on a shelf and gathered dust. The day before the trip, the team had a "dress rehearsal" to make sure that all the boys were comfortable in their shoes and socks. Then the head took a team photograph.

It seemed as if every child in the school, plus all

the people from the surrounding villages, turned out to wave the buses off that morning. Before they left, the headmaster told everyone to be quiet for a few minutes while he prayed for safe travel, and for the boys to play their best.

As the buses pulled out of the village, everyone on board began to sing. They had left early, because the headmaster had asked the drivers to do a tour of the city, so that the team and their supporters could see some places of interest.

Shema was so happy. He was seated next to Mama Grace, or rather, he should have been seated, but in his excitement he was bouncing up and down most of the time! He had so much to feel happy about! He had passed his end of term exams with flying colours and would soon be going up to Class Three.

He was wearing a brand new T-shirt which Ishimwe had bought for him when she was in the market. It had a gorilla on the front, like the ones he had seen with Sam in the wild. He had a few bananas and a bottle of water for the trip. He also had Mama Grace to take care of him on this big adventure! It was exciting when the bus reached the main road. There was so much to look at. After a while the bus wound its way down a hill into a steep valley, where there was a large river. Beside the river men and women were cutting what seemed to be huge, green reeds and loading them on to a truck.

"What is that?" Shema asked Mama Grace.

"It is sugar cane," she answered. "It will go to the factory and be made into sugar, like the sugar we put in our tea. It's very good to eat just as it is. We used to do that when we were young. We cut the long stalk into pieces about 25 centimetres long, stripped off the outer skin, then chewed on it! It is very sweet, in fact it is one of the most delicious things in the world! When you have eaten all the sugar you spit out the stringy fibre which is left! Oh how I loved that as a child!" she added wistfully.

"It looks a bit like the bamboo that the gorillas eat," commented Shema.

One of the parents in the bus called out to the driver. "Please can we stop for a moment?"

"All right," he replied and waved his hand up and down slowly to indicate to the other bus that he was pulling over. Both buses stopped and the children were allowed to get out for a few minutes. One poor little boy was sick as the road had been so bumpy.

Mama Grace pulled her purse out of her huge, old bag. She went over to the people cutting the sugar cane and asked them if they would cut her some sticks into pieces, enough for everyone. The men peeled them with their large machetes and gave them all pieces of sugar cane to chew. It was delicious! Many of the children had not tasted it before, and many of the adults felt like children again as they chewed the sticky stalks!

"Thank you so much Mama Grace," said the

headmaster. The extra sugar will give the team more energy. I think I will buy a little more for them to have just before the match!"

Soon everyone was back in the buses and they were heading up the hill on the other side of the river. Before long the countryside changed and there were more and more houses clustered along the roadside. Everything in the city was interesting to these village people. The noise, the bustle, the houses, the shops, the streets with street lamps and traffic lights, policemen directing the traffic and even parks with lovely trees and fountains! They drove past the parliament building, the law courts, then the Presidential Palace. They weren't allowed inside the gates, of course!

For Shema, the best part of the sight-seeing trip was when they were taken to the airport terminal building at Kanombe. They were allowed off the bus and upstairs to a viewing gallery so that they could watch real planes taking off from the runway.

"One day, that will be me in one of those planes," Shema said to Sam

Sam nodded. "You will be the best pilot in Rwanda."

Mama Grace smiled. She knew Shema's ambition to become an airline pilot. She remembered the time, not so very long ago, when Shema and Sam had whirled about her living room pretending to be planes!

Finally, the buses drove up to the stadium where the match was to be played. Everyone got off the buses and the team went one way with the headmaster, while the football teacher, parents and friends were led through a tunnel to the seats which had been allocated to them. Shema and Mama Grace looked around with amazement. It was a huge stadium, bigger than any building they had ever been in before in their lives! Already the stadium was filling up with people gathering to watch the game. An attendant pointed out to them the place where the VIPs sat, under a special awning. "The President and the First Lady are coming to watch," he informed them. "The President is very interested in school children and also in football!" he added.

They were trying to take this in when they heard music and a military band began to march around the arena. How smart they looked! Shema felt so proud to be Rwandan! The flag was flying and presently everyone stood to welcome the President and his wife. The supporters were so excited as they had a really good view of their tall, dignified leader and his beautiful wife in her ceremonial costume.

Next, the national drummers and dancers came into the arena and entertained the crowd. It was all so exciting and they were brilliant! Shema had never seen dancers or drummers like this! He wanted to remember everything so that he could share it with his brother and sister.

Then there was a drum roll . . . and out came the teams, led by their captains. First came the team from Kibungo, a town in the south of the country. They looked very smart in red and white stripes. A huge cheer went up for them. Then out came Sam, leading his team in their green and white strip. The supporters cheered with all their might. Everyone stood up and sang the national anthem, led by the band. Mama Grace wiped a tear from her face. She felt so proud of her country which was working so hard to recover from the terrible war, and she felt so proud of her young son. "I wish your dad could see you now!" she thought. Her thoughts were interrupted by the referee blowing his whistle as the match began!

The Kibungo boys all looked somewhat bigger and stronger than the village lads, but Sam and his team were able to run fast and were very good at passing. Mama Grace didn't really understand much about football, so Shema tried to explain to her what was happening as they went along. She was jumping up and down and shouting like a child in her excitement, and at one point was sweating so much on her forehead that Shema got quite worried; he was relieved when she sat down and drank some water!

At half time there was no score: the teams were very evenly matched. Inside the changing rooms, the headmaster spoke to his boys. "You are great," he said, "and I am so proud of you all. Keep up the good work. You are just as good as the Kibungo team. You can win!

But win or lose, remember, no foul play and do your best. That is what the President wants to see!"

"Yes sir," said the boys. Sam hesitantly asked him, "Sir, would it be all right if I played in my bare feet? You see, I am just not used to shoes and socks. Somehow, I think I am more likely to score if I have no shoes on."

The headmaster thought for a moment and consulted the football teacher. "I am sure that would be all right," he answered. "There doesn't appear to be anything in the rule book about shoes."

"Thank you sir," said Sam as he pulled off his new trainers and the socks. Several other members of the team did the same.

When they came out of the tunnel for the second half, some people were laughing at Sam and his friends because they were bare-footed. They took no notice and the game resumed. After just a few minutes one of his team mates headed the ball to Sam inside the penalty box and with a great strike he beat the goalkeeper! The cheering resounded all round the stadium.

The goal had worried the Kibungo boys. They played with more vigour and soon equalised with a fantastic goal. 1-1! The game was getting even more exciting! Sam and his team seemed to be getting more possession of the ball but just couldn't beat the brilliant Kibungo goal keeper. Then one of the village players was fouled, leaving him injured and unable to play on. The sub came on, but Sam knew he wasn't such a good player. However, they now had a free kick! Sam took the kick. He whispered a prayer and with his bare foot struck a superb drive that evaded the other team's defensive wall and flew into the net! The cheers of their supporters lifted them, even though the team were feeling very tired. The Kibungo boys fought on. Their defenders did a good job intercepting the ball time and time again, and then they managed to score again! All the boys were getting very tired, and in spite of all their supporters cheering, the village team could not prevent the Kibungo boys scoring a decisive third goal.

At the final whistle Sam was sorry that his team had lost, but it had been a very good game and every player had given one hundred per cent. As the headmaster had said, "only one team can win".

The team lined up and were led up to the President. He smiled at Sam, and said, "Well done, young man. One day you will play for our country, I am sure! I used to play bare-footed, too. Never worry about people laughing at you – do what you know to be right." With these inspiring words, he hung a medal around Sam's neck and handed him the runners-up trophy. It may not have been the silver cup, but Sam still felt very proud and happy.

In the changing room, the headmaster told them how very proud he was. The team had shown that even though a person might live in a poor village, in a poor area like theirs, they could still excel.

Once they had calmed down, they found that the national press wanted photographs of the teams and the trophies, so they had to line up on the pitch again. When it was all over, they were shown the showers and had such fun. None of them had ever had a hot shower before and they just wanted to stay under the water for ages! Their teacher had to hurry them up because the buses needed to take them home.

Once they were dressed and back at the buses, there were many hugs from proud parents and friends. The headmaster was beaming from ear to ear. "Guess what!" he told the group. "The President has given money as a prize to the school! He told me, first to get you all some coke and samosas. Then we are to think of something the school really needs and buy it. He would like to visit us and see what we have done with the gift! Can you imagine, the President coming to visit our school!"

Everyone cheered again, before piling into the buses. They drove to a nearby shopping centre to get their treats, then finally began the long journey home. By this time it was getting dark and most of the children fell asleep after all the excitement of a never-to-be-forgotten day!

SEVENTEEN

Christmas!

The football final occupied everyone's thoughts and conversation for days afterwards, for no school in the whole region had ever had such fame! However, term finished and Christmas was approaching. The young people who were away at secondary school returned, including Grace, Sam's sister. Mama Grace was delighted to have her daughter home again. Grace was pleased to see how Maji and Michal helped in the garden and what a good friend Shema was to Sam. She enjoyed talking to Ishimwe, too, and was so pleased that her dressmaking business was going well.

Ishimwe shared with Grace the secret she had been planning for the last few months. Grace thought that buying chickens was a great idea and promised to help. The chickens were not to eat, but to look after, and produce eggs. They were to have a proper coop. She and Grace went to the carpenter in Mama Grace's village and he promised to make it for a good price and deliver it just before Christmas.

Frida and Ishimwe had been planning a joint Christmas meal for their families. In Rwanda,

Christmas is a special feast day, kept to celebrate the birth of Jesus. Often the children might have gifts of new clothes, but there are no Christmas trees or pretty lights or stockings to be filled with toys. Even so, it is a special time and everyone looks forward it.

The girls had saved up to buy some beef, to make into a delicious stew with tomatoes, little aubergines and onions. They had also bought some beef masala powder to flavour the stew. Frida had a little sweetcorn saved which they could roast in the embers of the fire. It was hard to get vegetables in the dry season, but they would cook dry beans and have rice and maybe even plantain bananas called matoke, if they were available in the market. The girls had such fun planning. Frida was so much happier these days, and often sang as she went about her work.

One day Frida had a great surprise! She was sitting outside her little house on a stool and making a basket. Her baskets were just as good as Janette's and the girls now had a good income from selling them. She was singing a little "thank you" song to God when she heard the noise of a car coming into the village. For a moment she froze with fear. Was Justin coming again? Janette and Michal were in the back of the house, cleaning the rice for supper, and came rushing through when they heard the car engine, for such a thing was rare in their village.

"Run and fetch Delphine quickly, please," she asked Michal. He was the fastest runner in the family and ran at top speed to the social worker's house. The car stopped outside their house and Frida began to shake. Janette was worried, too, and stood very close to her. The car door opened and a man, woman and child got out.

The child ran as fast as his little fat legs would take him and flung himself into Frida's lap. When she saw who it was, she stopped being frightened and beamed from ear to ear. "It's Manweli! Come here and cuddle Frida!" She found tears of delight pouring down her face, for she had missed the little boy so much.

Libertina and her husband had got out of the car, too. They greeted Frida warmly. Just then, up ran Michal, followed by Delphine. "What is the problem?" puffed Delphine, all out of breath.

"Oh, there isn't a problem after all, but I thought there was," said Frida, smiling. "When I heard a car, I thought Justin had returned and I was very scared. Then dear little Manweli toddled up to me!"

Ishimwe, Shema and Maji came over when they heard all the fuss and when everyone had been introduced and tea was served, Libertina spoke. "I am glad that you are all well, but sorry that we frightened you, Frida. You need never fear Justin again, he has been found to be a really bad man and is in prison. But little Manweli loves Frida so much and still keeps calling her name, even though he settled happily at our house. Could we sometimes come and visit like we have today?"

Frida looked at the social worker. "Auntie, is that possible? I would love to see Manweli as he grows up! It would be so sad if he forgot me. And, of course, I would like to see his uncle and aunt, too," she added politely.

"Of course you may!" answered Delphine. "This is your home and you are free to have friends visit whenever you like."

* * *

One morning, not long after, Delphine, the pastor and his wife called a meeting for all the older children who were not able to go to school. They talked about their new Hope Skills Centre project. Most of the young people were very enthusiastic about the idea. Ishimwe looked at Frida and they were both very excited. A chance to learn even though they could not go to school!

It had been decided to start the project after the long school holiday, when the rains began. Delphine had made a list of the sort of classes they hoped to run and the boys and girls were told to think about which class they wanted to join.

Frida hoped there would be someone to teach her hairdressing. All the children in the project would also have classes in literacy and numeracy. "Maybe I might still have a chance to become a nurse!" Ishimwe said excitedly to Frida.

"But you are already a fine dressmaker," her friend replied.

"I love sewing, but more than anything I want to help sick people," she replied, remembering the time when Maji had been very ill in the hospital and she had watched the nurses take care of him. Maybe even her dream would come true!

On Christmas Eve Ishimwe and Grace walked to the market to buy the surprise chickens for Maji and Shema. They were full of giggles and Mama Grace was happy that at last Ishimwe's secret plan was coming to pass. The market was very busy. Everyone was buying good food for the Christmas celebration!

The girls found two lovely speckled hens, then Ishimwe paid for them with the money she had saved so carefully over the last few months. After she had bought them, the hens' legs were tied with string and each girl held one carefully. At first the chickens squawked and fussed, but settled down as the girls smoothed their feathers and talked softly to them.

Ishimwe had a little money left over, enough to buy a few sweets for all her friends, and enough to give a "thank you" gift at church on Christmas Day.

When they arrived back at Ishimwe's house, everyone was outside admiring the new chicken house which had been delivered by the carpenter! There was great excitement as the hens were introduced to their new home. Shema and Maji jumped up and down and danced around when they discovered that the hens were their very own Christmas present! Shema decided to call his hen, "Rimwe" which means "one", so Maji immediately chose "Kabili" for his hen, which means "two". They decided that this had to be the best Christmas ever, even though Christmas Day hadn't yet arrived!

Christmas Day dawned hot and sunny. Ishimwe had made the boys new shorts and matching shirts, and had even made a new dress for herself. After breakfast, dressed in their new clothes, they called next door and presented Frida, Janette and Michal with some new clothes and some sweets. There was such excitement! Frida and Janette had made some lovely baskets for them, too. There was one each for the boys, to use when they collected the eggs from their hens, and two big baskets for Ishimwe to use for storing her rice and sugar.

Soon, they were all on their way to church. They were such a happy group running up the dusty path, joining many others on the way to celebrate this most special day, the birthday of Jesus, who loved them so much and whom they had grown to love. They had so much to be thankful for, and with Jesus in their lives, life was filled with hope!

Author's Note

Although here and there in this book the names of actual localities have been used, the Village of Hope is fictional, as are all the characters. The village, however, is typical of many villages built for child-headed families after the Rwandan Genocide of 1994.

Also available from Dernier Publishing for 8–11s:

I Want to Be an Airline Pilot
by Mary Weeks Millard

Shema, an eight-year-old Rwandan goatherd from a child-led family, has many adventures, including a goat eating his only T-shirt, a frightening visit to a medicine man and a dangerously close brush with a spitting black cobra! Through them all, little by little, Shema learns about "Mister God" and discovers that although he is an orphan, he has a Father in heaven who cares for him. A victorious, heart-warming story, with lovely background to life in rural Rwanda.

"I give this book 10/10." – Ellen

"A thrilling adventure story about three orphans' dreams coming true when their prayers were answered." – Jonathan

"I think this book is very good; it made me feel happy, sad and really excited. I think the most interesting part was when Shema faced the black cobra. It was also very moving when in the book Ishimwe starts to cry because her parents died. I really enjoyed this book, it is one of my favourites." – Kemi

ISBN 978 0 9536963 5 2

The Birthday Shoes
by Mary Weeks Millard

Emily Jane hates her new shoes until she finds that they hold an amazing secret! Join her as she goes on magical journeys to Africa, making new friends and some exciting discoveries about God.

> "My favourite part was when Emily Jane put on her shoes for the first time and ended up in Africa. It made me feel like I was there!" – Susanna

ISBN 978 0 9536963 8 3

Deepest Darkness
by Denise Hayward

Ten-year-old Abi suffers from terrible nightmares and her life is ruled by fear. On holiday in Canada, she makes a new friend who shows her through a series of adventures that true light shines, even in the deepest darkness.

> "This is a brilliant story . . . one of the best books I have read – EVER!" – Maddie

ISBN 978 0 9536963 6 9

By J.M. Evans for 8–11s:

The Treasure Hunt

Ravi, Debbie, Joel and Lance's first exciting mystery adventure. Who is in the back of the white lorry and why are they there? Prayer, faith and their Bible knowledge all help, but when the case takes an unexpected turn, the friends also need to be courageous and obedient.

"The best book I've ever read!" – Emily
"Brilliant!" – Ben

ISBN 978 0 9536963 1 4

Mystery in the Snow

Not long after solving their first mystery, Ravi, Debbie, Lance and Joel find themselves with another problem: Ravi's shed has been burgled. Can they find out who did it? The plot thickens as an old lady's handbag goes missing, then a cat disappears.

"I would definitely recommend it." – Joshua
"So exciting that I couldn't put it down!" – Lydia

ISBN 978 0 9536963 3 8